# GRAND   BARRAGE

# GRAND BARRAGE

BY

GUN BUSTER

Windrow&Greene

© 1994 Windrow & Greene Ltd.

First published 1944 by
Hodder & Stoughton Ltd.

This edition published 1994 by
Windrow & Greene Ltd.
19A Floral Street
London WC2E 9DS

A CIP record for this book is
available from the British Library

ISBN 1 85915 001 2

Printed and bound in Great Britain by
Biddles Ltd, Guildford and King's Lynn

# CONTENTS

## Part I

| CHAP. | | PAGE |
|---|---|---|
| I. | THE NIGHT BEFORE - - - - - | 7 |
| II. | FIRST ACCENTS OF DEFIANCE - - - | 13 |
| III. | ON LEAVE WITH A GHOST - - - - | 24 |
| IV. | REDUCED TO THE RANKS - - - - | 35 |
| V. | GUNNER ON RECONNAISSANCE - - - | 46 |
| VI. | GUN OPERATIONS ROOM - - - - | 56 |
| VII. | ENTER THE LUFTWAFFE - - - - | 67 |
| VIII. | ATTACK ON THE *ILLUSTRIOUS* - - - | 76 |
| IX. | A BIT OF VICTORY - - - - - | 86 |

## Part II

| I. | ATTACK FROM THE SEA - - - - | 95 |
|---|---|---|
| II. | THE BATTERY COMMANDER INTERVENES | - 106 |
| III. | RETURN OF THE LUFTWAFFE - - - | - 112 |
| IV. | THE STORM BURSTS ANEW - - - | - 117 |
| V. | VON OPPENHEIM - - - - | - 126 |
| VI. | " NO FRIENDLY AIRCRAFT AIRBORNE " | - 134 |

# CONTENTS

| CHAP. | | | | | | PAGE |
|---|---|---|---|---|---|---|
| VII. | BARRAGE IN FULL BLAST - | - | - | - | - | 143 |
| VIII. | UNDER SIEGE - | - | - | - | - | 149 |
| IX. | GUNNER ON PARADE - | - | - | - | - | 157 |
| X. | IN SEARCH OF BLUE LABEL | - | - | - | - | 163 |
| XI. | ONE SUNDAY ON THE GUN-SITE - | - | - | - | 169 |
| XII. | EVACUATION - | - | - | - | - | 180 |
| XIII. | EPILOGUE - | - | - | - | - | 185 |

# PART I

THE Colonel of the 777th H.A.A. Regiment, and the Adjutant were enjoying a late whisky on the verandah outside the Mess at Fort Pedro.

Behind the island the sun had sunk in a cloudless splendour of orange and gold. And across Marsamuscetto Harbour they had watched with the same rapt attention as so often before, the narrow, terraced streets of Valetta fill with rich, deep-purple shadows haunted, so it seemed, by the ghosts of the white buildings and residences of the city. As the twilight thickened the familiar features disappeared entirely. The twin towers of the Cathedral of St. John were swallowed up in the darkness along with the wireless masts on top of the R.A. Headquarters. Above the blacked-out city very white stars began to burn high in the sky. A murmur of the sea drifted up from the little beach at the base of the Fort. The hot Mediterranean night succeeded the hot Mediterranean day.

The Colonel emptied his glass.

" Last time we shall see it quite like that for many a day," he observed, gazing over the dark harbour in the direction of Valetta.

" Yes. I suppose it's sure to get knocked about a bit despite our best efforts," said the Adjutant.

" I wasn't thinking of bombs just then," the Colonel replied reflectively. " Next time we see Valetta it'll be a city in the front-line of battle. So far it has only been on the fringe. We shall be looking at it with other eyes. That makes a difference."

After a pause he added : " I shall be sorry to see it damaged. I've been stationed here over five years. I've grown an affection for the little place."

He was quite sincere. The streets of Valetta—not to mention those of Hong Kong and Singapore—were far more

familiar to him than the streets of London. The Colonel liked
foreign service, and eighteen of the twenty-four years of his
military life had been spent abroad.

" I wonder how the Maltese will stand up to it," remarked
the Adjutant.

" Hard to guess."

" They seem patriotic enough."

" That'll help. But with air-raids it's largely a matter of
nerves. The Maltese are volatile. Nice fair-weather people.
I hope they'll prove as good in foul weather. They're in for
an ordeal."

" The declaration of War must have hit them a hell of a
smack, sir," said the Adjutant. " They've been so confident
all along that the Italians would stay out. They boasted
they knew their Mussolini."

" They didn't know their Hitler," laughed the Colonel.
" Mussolini does what he's told."

" D'you think he'll try to invade ? "

" It'll be wise to expect everything. Personally I hope he
won't—just yet. When I contemplate invasion it's a decided
comfort that we only have to think at present in terms of
the Regia Aeronautica and not of the Luftwaffe. As you
know, we've only three planes on the island."

" Good old Faith, Hope, and Charity," murmured the
Adjutant using the pet names bestowed by the Maltese upon
the trio of obsolete Gloucester-Gladiators which in June 1940
comprised the sum total of Malta's air fighting force. " After
all the dreary months they've spent providing our gunners
with ack-ack practice they'll be glad of the change. And
so shall we. It's a relief, sir, isn't it, to know we're going
into action at last."

" Yes. I'm anxious to see the results of all that practice,"
said the Colonel, with a smile.

" And thank God the sirocco isn't blowing," added the
Adjutant, fervently. " I prefer my baptism of bombs without
the perspiration."

They rose together and entered the Mess. Originally a
Navy Mess it was furnished with that satisfying blend of
simplicity and comfort which is the knack of the Navy. For
the time being the Gunners were sharing it with the " Sub-
Mariners," the officers of the submarines based on the island,
who had their quarters in the barracks not far away. To-night

the Sub-Mariners were conspicuous by their absence. They were already at sea, seeking out Mussolini's armada.

Passing through the deserted ante-room the Colonel paused in front of the Bets Register, a long sheet of paper tacked to the wall and ruled in four columns. On it were recorded all the bets made from time to time in the Mess. The Colonel's eye attached itself to one of the more recent entries. In the first column he read :

" The C.O. says Musso will declare war by June 12th," and underneath the words :

" The Lieutenant-Quartermaster says ' Nuts ' "—this being the time-honoured and unequivocal form in which all the bets were recorded.

In the second column was the date of the bet, " June 3," and in the third column the stakes : " One Havana cigar." The fourth column still awaited the entry of the date on which the bet had been lost and won, and the red tick indicating that the wager had been paid.

The Colonel looked at his bet meditatively. He had made it after hearing the news of the Dunkirk evacuation. It had seemed a sure hunch. On the wall of the ante-room the round Navy clock registered ten p.m.

" In two hours," he said, with a touch of solemnity, " I shall be entitled to explore all the mysteries of the Quarter-master's boasted Havana."

The Adjutant laughed. " Am I to assume, sir, from your pessimistic tone, you'd rather have lost ? "

" You can assume I'm going to get what sleep I can while I have the chance," replied the Colonel, with another glance at the clock. " We can't count on more than two hours. And it may be less. I don't trust Mussolini. I advise you to get some sleep, too."

In the Mess itself, where the big panorama of Grand Harbour hung on the wall, a lonely Navy steward was endeavouring to put a superfine gloss on the already super-latively polished oblong mahogany dining-table, totally unimpressed by the fact that the War had now arrived at Malta's door-step. Here the Colonel parted from the Adjutant but, instead of going straight to bed as he had intended, he decided on a last look round. Mounting the flight of stone steps leading to the ramparts of the Fort he made his way towards the sand-bagged Command Post. Nearby he could

distinguish the dark, innocent-looking shapes of the parapher-
nalia of his own corner of the war—the predictor, like a giant
box-camera on a tripod, the ten-foot height-finder, and on
another tripod the T.I. (telescope indentification) which
enables the observer to identify an approaching plane, and to
give to the predictor the bearing it is flying in from, and the
angle of sight. As the Colonel approached, the shadowy form
of the spotter on duty, field-glasses in hand, materialised out
of the darkness.

Lifting the blanket hanging over the door of the Command
Post the Colonel ducked his head and entered. The place was
lit by a hurricane lamp, and the heat was sub-tropical. At a
little table, a message-pad in front of him, earphones clamped
to his head, sat a sweating, half-naked telephonist reading a
thriller, as though his own situation was not about to provide
sufficient excitement for him. Now and then, to test the line
to Gun Operations Room away in Valetta, which co-ordinated
the firing of all the A.A. gun sites on the island, he rang the
bell of his instrument. A voice replied. Whereupon the
telephonist said : " O.K.," and resumed his thriller. Sometimes he varied the routine by asking : " Heard anything
yet ? " But the reply was always in the negative. Dozing
in his bunk lay the Gun Position Officer's " ack," a lance-
sergeant ; and the G.P.O. himself sat at another camp table
scribbling a letter home. All ready in front of him was his
plotting board, a bold, squared, outline map of Malta done in
black and white, and covered with talc. Its virgin surface
awaited the defilement by chinagraph pencils that would
immediately follow the receipt of an A.K. message from Gun
Operations Room announcing the approach of the first raiders.

" I hear your tennis parties at Sliema are going to be badly
curtailed by Italians, Bruce," said the Colonel, with a
twinkle.

" Yes, sir," grinned the G.P.O. " It's grand, isn't it, to
be going to have a crack at them."

" Nothing on the board, of course ? "

" Nothing, sir."

" It won't be long now. . . . I think I'll take a look at the
guns before turning in."

Accompanied by the G.P.O. the Colonel crossed the iron
bridge over the dry moat surrounding the Fort, and walked
towards the gun pits.

The 777th Regiment consisted of two batteries, twelve guns apiece, stationed on four different sites, one of which was Fort Pedro. Some of the guns were mobile 3.7's, and others 4.5's. Don-Troop of four 3.7's was stationed at Fort Pedro, which was also Regimental Headquarters. In addition the regiment possessed one of the Naval eight-barrel pom-poms, known throughout the Services as " Chicago pianos," from their organ-pipe appearance. This was planted on a site in Valetta near the Dockyard, the most unpopular site of all with the gunners because no smoking was allowed.

The 777th was a Regular field regiment that had been diverted to " Ack-Ack " when war broke out. The bulk of the men knew all there was to be known of the pleasures and discomforts of service in Jubbulpore, Aden, Singapore and Hong Kong. Their conversation was interlarded with strange words picked up during their long sojourn in garrison depots in India and Malaya. To most of them the Quatab Mirrah* meant far more than Nelson's Column. When war broke out they were in the stage technically known as " sweating the trooper." In other words they were bound for England and home, which they hadn't seen for many years. They bore the disappointment of finding themselves garrisoning Malta instead, with the usual mixture of grumbling and philosophy. What they found much harder to bear was the nine months of enforced inactivity that followed, an inactivity disturbed only by the daily monotony of ack-ack practice, and " standing-to " whenever a ship was signalled approaching the island. It was the latter diversion that came near to breaking their hearts. Hence it will be understood that they welcomed with a relief such as only utterly " browned off " ack-ack gunners are capable of, the news that Mussolini was at last coming to play with them. It wasn't martial joy, and it wasn't heroics. It was *just sheer thankfulness that something had happened to put an end to their boredom.

In the hot darkness, with the white stars burning overhead and uneasy Valetta crouched on its peninsula across the harbour, a humped patch black as the night itself, the Colonel and G.P.O. proceeded to the nearest gun-pit. The limber-

* A tall, round tower at a Gunner practice camp near Delhi ; and famous among artillerymen as an aiming-point.

gunner on duty was fondling the breach of a 3.7 with an oily
rag. The long, graceful muzzle of the gun pointed sharply
at the sky over the invisible city to whose protection it was
dedicated. The warm sea-laden air took the smell of
lubricating oil and mineral jelly, the smell of steel, and
perhaps the faintest possible reminiscence of cordite-fumes—
that blended, indefinable odour which is always associated
with the guns, and is as characteristic in its way as the
smell of stables—and handed the mixture back to the Colonel
in a bouquet that, being a fond Gunner, he sniffed
appreciatively. From the sand-bagged shelter close by,
where the gun-crew had their quarters, came the sound of
a mouth-organ playing " Roll Out the Barrel." Floating
out into the unbroken silence of the vast, portentous
Mediterranean night, wherein Death and Destruction were
already massing for their initial assault, the simple strains
sounded forlorn and plaintive, and pathetically human.

Followed by the G.P.O. the Colonel pulled back the tarpaulin
and stepped inside the shelter. The virtuoso on the mouth-
organ, his naked torso tanned the hue of teak by the Maltese
sun, was sitting up in his bunk jerking his head and shoulders
to and fro in time with the music. Seven or eight other
gunners were spread around smoking, chatting and dozing.
By the light of a solitary candle stuck in a beer bottle the
sergeant who was No. 1 of the gun was fiercely studying the
silhouettes of Italian machines in the latest aeroplane
identification pamphlet, and wondering which of them he'd
be spotting first.

At the Colonel's appearance the mouth-organ and the
conversation died away. The sergeant jumped to his feet,
but the roof was too low for him to straighten himself to his
full height. Both he and the Colonel were tall men and they
stood before one another as though bowing in mutual
politeness.

" What type of plane have you decided it's going to be,
sergeant ? " inquired the Colonel, good-humouredly.

" I think they'll be Savoia 79's, sir. That's their most
useful bomber, I'm told."

"Not a bad deduction. But if you want to be right first
time take my advice and look up Macchi in your pamphlet."

" Macchi," echoed the sergeant. " What makes you think
that, sir ? "

" They'll probably start with a bit of reconnaissance,"
replied the Colonel.

He said good night and turned to go. Just before the
tarpaulin dropped behind him he looked back.

" By the way, sergeant," he said, with a slight stiffening
of tone, " it has gone ' Lights Out ' ".

" Yes, sir."

A heavy puff immediately followed and the shelter was
plunged into sudden darkness.

As the Colonel and his companion continued their progress
to the next gun-pit they heard the mouth-organ strike up
again. The teak-torsoed gunner was putting all his feelings
of the moment into the refrain of " Home, Sweet Home."
The irony was unescapable. It did not, nor was it intended
to, escape the Colonel. Unseen, his features relaxed into an
amused smile.

" Have you ever noticed, Bruce," he said, " what a great
variety of emotions that despised tune is capable of expressing
in the hands of a gifted artist such as our friend yonder ? "


## II—First Accents of Defiance

Six-thirty a.m. The day promised to be another scorcher.
By now Malta had been at war with Mussolini for exactly
six and a half hours. But Valetta had enjoyed a quiet night,
if not a peaceful one. The infantry coast patrols had found
nothing of importance to report from the sea, and the island's
R.D.F. station nothing from the air. At Fort Pedro the Gun
Position Officer's plotting board still maintained its pristine
purity of surface. Nevertheless, Valetta had no illusions
about what might be expected any moment. Already many
of the shopkeepers in the Strada Reale and the Strada
Stretta had decided to keep their shutters up. Impressed by
the Governor's order that in the event of an air-raid no one
was to be allowed in the streets, the inhabitants were already
chary of venturing from their houses without good reason.
The few who were out and about gathered in small groups
and exchanged their hopes and fears in subdued tones, at
the same time unconsciously letting their glances rove in
the direction of the speckless blue sky.

Around the gun-pits at the Fort the gunners of Don-Troop were engaged in their morning toilette. Their quarters were, in fact, practically an annexe to the gun-pits themselves. The men were allowed a bare thirty seconds to come into action from the first blast of the Command Post whistle announcing an "Alert." So it meant living virtually on top of the guns, day and night.

The sudden shout of " Grub's up ! " speeded their matutinal ablutions. From the cook-house beside the Mess half a dozen cooks appeared on the bridge across the moat laden with breakfast, dixies of steaming tea, slopping over the sides, a mound of slices of bread and butter piled-up on a dixie lid, a couple of long loaves, and two dixies the contents of which remained to be divulged. As the cooks approached the first gun-pit, the fair, curly-headed bombardier, who had just finished shaving in a bit of broken mirror propped on the parapet, regarded these two dixies with a suspicious stare.

" Not sausages again, I hope ? " he demanded.

The cooks grinned.

" Blimey," cried the bombardier. " Ain't there any more bacon left in the world."

Whereupon a fusillade of chaff and caustic comment from the gunners was levelled at the cooks.

" Why can't you make it fish-cakes ? "

" Hi, cookie, don't slop our char (tea) about like that. Save some for us to drink. . . ."

" Hope the bloody stuff is sweeter than it was yesterday. . . ."

Around the gun-pits the men, naked to the waist and clad only in khaki-drill shorts and plimsolls, clustered round the cooks to have the food dished out into their mess-tins, and sat about on sandbags in the brilliant, warm, sunshine, chewing vigorously.

Not far away in the Command Post the Gun Position Officer, after being on duty all night was waiting to be relieved, and thinking how satisfactory it would be to have a wash and shave and get down to a breakfast. A new telephonist was on duty, a cup of tea beside him, munching a sausage sandwich. The sight sharpened the G.P.O.'s appetite, though he regretfully recognised that the omens were against there being fried bacon in the Mess.

Suddenly the telephonist, half-choking himself to get rid

of a mouthful of unchewed food, seized his pencil and shouted :

"Alert ! . . ."

Galvanised into wide wakefulness the G.P.O. hung over his shoulder straining to catch the fateful words coming through from Gun Operations Room in Valetta. All he could hear was a nasal twang in the earphones. He glanced at his watch. It was six forty-six.

"Alert ! . . . Alert . . . Alert . . ." wrote the telephonist on his pad, repeating each word back as it came over.

"Alert ! . . ." roared the G.P.O. at the door of the shelter.

Immediately the air was torn by a blast from the whistle of the G.P.O.'s "Ack." And before the third blast had died away they could hear the "Raid Warning" sirens wailing over Malta for the first time in dead earnest.

Around the gun-pits the crews dropped the remains of their unfinished breakfast and dashed to their gun positions. The curly-headed bombardier came running from the direction of the latrines, a sausage sandwich in one hand and holding up his shorts with the other. Being No. 3 on the gun it was necessary for him to have at least one hand free instantaneously for working the dial that put on the quadrant elevation. He hesitated not a second. His shorts dropped to his ankles and he stood naked save for his tin-hat and his plimsolls.

"It's an air-raid, not a strip-tease," hissed the sergeant. And a guffaw swept the gun-pit.

The only response from the bombardier was the broad grin to which he owed his nickname, "Smiler." He kicked himself clear of his shorts and settled his bare posterior on the iron saddle by the side of the gun. On the other side, with the gun between them, sat the No. 2, a serious-faced, dark youth who being named Baker was always called "Doughy." He was a lance-bombardier, and had charge of the traverse dial. These dials were connected to the predictor by a cable. They each possessed a predictor pointer, electrically controlled, and a manual pointer moved by turning the dial handle. During action the manual pointer on both elevating and traverse dials had to be kept moving by the layers so as to be always coincident with the predictor pointer.

In the Command Post the telephonist was busy pencilling-in

the details of the A.K. message that was being shouted through from Gun Operations Room. At the head of his form he wrote the serial number of the raid : " One." Little did the G.P.O. watching him impatiently, dream that the time would come when those serial numbers would total up to over two thousand. Under the various alphabetical letters the telephonist continued to enter up the information he was receiving :

" One plus," meaning that one or more hostile planes were approaching.

" 250 degrees," the bearing they were coming in from.

" 8,000," the height in feet.

" 17,000," the range in yards.

And so on.

As fast as the details left the telephonist's pencil the G.P.O. drew lines and measured angles on the talc-surfaced plotting-board, and hastened outside to give the spotter a rough idea of the direction in which to search the sky for the enemy. They stood beside one another for a brief while, field-glasses fastened to their eyes. At first they could see nothing, the dry brilliance of the atmosphere being a hindrance to good vision up aloft. Leaning against the brownish, weather-stained limestone ramparts of the Fort, clad in a dressing-gown, the Colonel also was raking the sky with his glasses.

Suddenly the sergeant of No. 1 gun bawled :

" Plane ! . . ."

Within his roar there lurked a note of triumph. The spotter understood it and frowned slightly. Though almost simultaneously with the sergeant both he and the G.P.O. had shouted : " There it is," he knew that the sergeant, with his astounding eagle eye, had once more beaten the binoculars, and won his long-standing bet that he would be first in the Troop, spotter or no spotter, to detect the enemy.

Now the spotter was busy with his Telescope Identification, adjusting it all the time with milled screws so that the plane should not escape from his field of vision.

" It's a Macchi," he exclaimed.

All over the island the sirens ., .e still rising and falling in their doleful wail.

Standing by the T.I. the Gun Position Officer's " Ack' read the bearing and angle of sight and shouted them to the height-finder and the predictor crew.

" Bearing, Three-O . . . Angle, One-Five degrees. . . ."

" Height-finder on target," its No. 1 shouted back in a second or two, to be followed immediately by No. 1 of the predictor :

" Predictor on target . . ."

" First, Sixteen-thousand . . ." yelled No. 1 on the height-finder, giving the range.

Through his megaphone the Gun Position Officer shouted to the predictor :

" Set Sixteen-thousand . . ."

" Sixteen-thousand set . . ." came the reply.

The wailing sirens all over the island died away as if exhausted by their effort.

" Section on target . . ." roared the Gun Position Officer's " Ack " to the G.P.O.

For a few seconds silence enveloped the gun site, a silence only broken by the far-off drone of the approaching plane and, close at hand, the quiet ticking of the predictor mechanism. In No. 3 gun-pit the naked Smiler and Doughy Baker on the other side of the gun were intently absorbed in keeping the mechanical pointers on their dials coincident with the predictor hands, wherever the latter moved. In response to their efforts the long tapering muzzle of the gun moved with heavy stealth across the sky.

" Vertical steady . . ."

" Lateral steady . . ."

The two reports from the predictor crew rang out almost simultaneously.

" Fire ! . . ." shouted the G.P.O.

But the guns did not fire. It was not their order. It was addressed to the predictor crew.

" Fuse Two-O," the No. 4 called out. He was predicting for the guns the fuse that would be the correct one by the time they fired.

" Fuse Two-O," roared the G.P.O.'s megaphone to the gun-pits.

The shells were stacked in wooden ammunition racks lining both sides of the gun-pits. It was fixed ammunition, shell and cartridge combined, and to save time was all pre-fused. Each shell bore the fuse-setting chalked on its base.

From the gun-pits came the clink of the shells as they dropped into the loading trays. They were rammed home, and the breeches closed behind with a clang. Again silence descended on the site, the silence now of immediate expectation. Above, the hostile plane droned louder. Across the harbour the white buildings of Valetta, bathed in the brilliant sunlight, stood out against the blue background of the sky and the Mediterranean, with a clear-cut, cameo-like beauty. A great hush seemed to have descended upon her streets. That faint, indefinable murmur that surrounds the presence of cities like an aura, the echoing pulse of life and activity, no longer manifested itself. For the moment the city seemed to hold its breath.

At the predictor the No. 4 was attentively watching the curve of his fuse dial. Just before the predicted fuse number came on the curve he yelled :

" Fire ! . . ."

" Fire ! . . ." roared the G.P.O.'s megaphone almost at the same moment.

In the gun-pits the sergeants' voices bawled the echoes : " No. 1, Fire ! . . ." " No. 3, Fire ! . . ." " No. 4, Fire ! . . ." " No. 2, Fire ! . . ."

The guns thundered. With a loud swish the shells tore into the blue sky, half-emptying the gun-pits of air by force of suction. All over the island other heavy batteries came into action. The limestone rocks and bastions reverberated with the boom, boom, boom.

Malta's first accents of defiance. . . .

Thousands of feet aloft, in a heaven of exquisite light and purity, white puffs of smoke from the bursting 3.7's, and darker puffs from the 4.5's, began to crowd in upon the course of the tiny aeroplane that was flying towards Valetta from the sea.

" Pedro shot . . ." the telephonist reported to Gun Operations Room to inform them that the site was in action.

From the direction of the height-finder, mingled with the roar of the guns, came the toneless chant of the No. 1 announcing the shortening of the range :

" Fifteen thousand . . . Fourteen-four hundred . . . Thirteen-eight hundred. . . ."

The predictor followed suit. Again and again the fuse was shortened. And in the gun-pits the deliberate, pounding rhythm of the 3.7's continued unfalteringly.

The plane, a lone Macchi out on a reconnaissance, flew

18

over the city at a height of about eleven thousand feet. In five minutes it had passed out of range.

" Stop loading . . . Stand easy . . .", ordered the Gun Position Officer.

In the sudden silence the gun teams busied themselves stacking-up the empties and re-arranging the ammunition in the racks. Before long the " All Clear " arrived from Gun Operations Room, and at the same time the sirens announced the fact to the island. A couple of cooks, carrying dixies of red-hot tea wended their way to the gun-pits shouting " Any more for any more." And with fresh, steaming draughts the sweating gunners prepared to wash down their interrupted breakfast.

Relieved at last by a subaltern, the Gun Position Officer, who was by no means dissatisfied it should have fallen to his lot to conduct the first real shoot, went and got his wash and shave and then proceeded to the Mess. The Colonel and the Adjutant were already having breakfast.

" What did you think of the show, sir ? " he asked, sipping his coffee. " I noticed you on the ramparts letting nothing escape you."

" Not so bad for a first time," said the Colonel, critically. " But there's room for improvement. We want a couple more raids to give us practice."

" It won't surprise me if we have them before the day's over," remarked the Adjutant. " That recce wasn't over for fun."

" Make it the morning and I'm inclined to agree with you," the Colonel nodded.

" You know, sir, that second burst of ours was pretty close," said the G.P.O., feeling that the C.O. was inclined to under-rate their efforts.

" It was, Bruce. But I don't propose that we shall start a count of near-misses. " Hits are good enough for me."

" I don't think that height-finder is much good," continued the Gun Position Officer. " As you know, sir, we've always had doubts about it."

" What's wrong ? "

" It seemed to be suffering all the time from an under-statement complex. Only a hundred feet, or so. But that's sufficient ! "

" We'll have to get it changed."

" I'll indent for one of the new No. 10's from Ordnance, sir," said the Adjutant.  " And let's hope we get it."

For some while they lingered over breakfast discussing the various points of their première with newcomers as they dropped in to the Mess.  Suddenly the shrill blasts of the Command Post whistle pierced the air.

" Here they are," shouted the Adjutant, jumping up.

" In earnest, this time," said the Colonel.

The G.P.O., now a spectator, strode over to the Command Post where his successor was already drawing and measuring on his plotting-board.  On the A.K. message form the telephonist had recorded among other data from Gun Operations Room the information that the raiders numbered " Four plus."

In a short while they materialised into half-a-dozen Savoia 79's, and they flew from the sea towards Valetta amid the roar of all the gun sites within range, to which was added the loud tattoo of the pom-poms of a destroyer in the Harbour. The flawless sky became speckled with hundreds of tiny, white, uncurling, cotton-wool tufts.  Circling inwards at a height of 14,000 feet the Savoias, one after the other released their cargoes on the Dockyard area, and for the first time the Maltese became acquainted with the sinister whine of falling bombs.  Watching the explosions with the Adjutant from the ramparts of the Fort, the Colonel saw huge plumes of whitish dust and smoke ascend into the air and gradually obliterate Valetta in a thick haze.  It looked as though the whole city was being laid in ruins.  Actually it was a dust phenomenon to which they were destined to grow well accustomed.  Most of the buildings were constructed of native limestone which had the characteristic of becoming pulverised on receiving a direct hit, filling the atmosphere with clouds of fine, choking dust.  It was so minute and penetrating that victims trapped in the debris of a raid ran a grave risk of being asphyxiated. On the other hand the limestone showed a wonderful power to resist the devastating effects of blast, with the result that damage was largely confined to the actual spot where the bomb had fallen.  Also, there were no fires to contend with.

The raid lasted half-an-hour.  Towards the close the spectators on the ramparts of the Fort heard a heavy explosion echo across the water and saw a colossal cloud of dust and smoke arise from a spot close to the entrance of

Grand Harbour. The Colonel happened to have his glasses focussed on the spot. He turned to the Adjutant.

" That one can't have dropped very far from Fort St. Elmo," he said with some concern. " I'll bet it shook up the Royal Malta Artillery gun site."

A quarter of an hour after the " All Clear " the telephonist in the Command Post was rung up from Gun Operations Room to take a message for the Colonel. Watching him write it down the G.P.O. read, word by word :

" Bomb fell at Dockyard Site. One man killed."

A runner took the message to the Adjutant, who was in the office with the Colonel.

" Bad news, sir," said the Adjutant, handing over the slip. " Our first casualty."

" I'll go over there at once," said the Colonel. " Get the Battery Commander. He can come with me."

They drove over the causeway separating the Fort from the mainland. As they approached Valetta the Colonel busied himself with a close scrutiny of the visible effects of the raid, As far as he could determine the material damage was not extensive. But what pleased him most was the absence of any signs of serious panic among the Maltese themselves. Obviously they had received a severe shaking-up. The streets were deserted save for scared family parties conveying themselves and their household goods, in donkey carts and handbarrows, to the security of air-raid shelters and outlying villages. Traffic was at a standstill except for an ambulance or two hurrying along the Strada Reale. Cinemas and cafés were closed. Practically all the shops were shuttered or boarded-up, and it was obvious that work had completely ceased. But all these symptoms the Colonel regarded as normal in the circumstances. Instinctively he felt that the city, though shaken, was sound.

" These people have had a bad shock, but they'll recover," he said to the Battery Commander as they drove along. " It will give them confidence, too, when we start knocking a few out of the sky."

" They've still got to learn what it feels like in the dark," the Battery Commander replied, with reserve. " Nothing ever feels quite so bad in the sunshine."

" Yes, I'm glad they didn't get their first taste last night," the Colonel admitted. " A mistake on the part of Mussolini."

The regiment's Dockyard site was a bare, level square on top of the bastions overlooking the Harbour, with an asphalt surface like a school playground. It consisted of a naval pom-pom and a wooden hut in which the crew lived and slept. As the Colonel approached, the sergeant in charge of the gun walked over to meet him.

" Who was it, sergeant ? "

" Gunner Sharman, sir. The telephonist. He was in the hut at the telephone. It got a direct hit. We've collected his remains. They're in that blanket."

By now they had reached the ruins of the hut. An army blanket, tied in a bundle, occupied the centre. All around was the wreckage of boards, scraps of sand-bags, clothing, food utensils, playing-cards and rifles. The blast had ripped away all their woodwork and twisted the barrels into grotesque shapes and knots.

" I'll arrange for the body to be collected and taken to the mortuary in Floriana," said the Colonel. " We'll have to have the burial to-day, also. Any of his special friends who wish to come to the funeral can do so if you arrange reliefs. Not more than six, though, all told. And that will include any from the Fort who want to go."

" Lance-bombardier Baker, Don-Troop, down at the Fort was his closest friend, sir," vouchsafed the sergeant. " I'd like to pay my last respects also, sir."

" All right," said the Colonel. " The Battery Commander can arrange that."

The funeral of the unfortunate gunner, who had achieved the doubtful distinction of being the first soldier to be killed in action on Malta, was fixed for six o'clock.

" Arrange for a coffin and get Driver Willis to have a Scammel and a trailer ready," the Colonel told the Adjutant, when he returned to the Fort. " Let the padre know all about the arrangements. Oh, and we must get hold of a Union Jack."

" That bomb you were interested in did fall on Fort St. Elmo, sir," the Adjutant mentioned. " Five Maltese gunners were killed, I'm told."

" Unlucky. It must have been about the last they dropped. Any planes down ? "

" I've heard of two, so far, sir."

" Gunners' first bag, I hope," said the Colonel.

Three more raids on the Dockyard and the aerodrome occupied the attention of the Fort between then and the time of the funeral. At a quarter to six, during a lull in the firing, the Scammel lorry drawing a trailer pulled up outside the mortuary at Floriana. Half a dozen men, including the sergeant and Lance-bombardier Baker jumped down and secured the coffin to the trailer. Over it they draped the Union Jack. The Colonel and the Battery Commander arrived in a car and the little procession made its way slowly towards St. Andrew's Cemetery, three miles from Sliema. The road wound round Marsamuscetto Harbour, past the end of the causeway to the Fort, and climbed the gentle slope to the cemetery. From the ramparts of the Fort the gunners could watch in the sunlight the last journey of their comrade.

" I didn't know Sharman well," said the curly-headed bombardier to the others. " But he always seemed a nice, harmless sort of chap. Doughy's going to miss him, though. They were stuck together like a stamp on an envelope." He paused and spat over the ramparts. " If it is any honour to be the first, I'm glad it didn't come my way," he added with conviction.

Meanwhile Lance-bombardier Doughy Baker, his serious face looking more serious than ever, was bearing the front right-hand corner of his friend's coffin on his shoulder. The pall-bearers, who had donned shirts and exchanged their plimsolls for ammunition boots, marched with slow, solemn step behind the Army chaplain towards the newly-dug grave. At the rear of the coffin followed the Colonel and the Battery Commander. Behind walked the sergeant dangling in each hand, like buckets, the tin-hats of the pall-bearers.

The chaplain gave Gunner Sharman the benefit of the full burial service during which Doughy stared straight ahead of him with an expression on his face as though he were wrestling with some new intricate problem that had beset him. And so he was. He was wondering what on earth he should do with his thoughts now he had no one to share them with.

The coffin was lowered into the grave and the mourners turned to depart.

" Only wanted a firing party to make the thing complete," murmured the Battery Commander to the Colonel.

23

Hardly had he spoken when the sirens began to wail over the island and soon the guns of Fort Pedro roared their salvoes against a fresh wave of raiders.

" There's the firing party," said the Colonel.

### III—On Leave with a Ghost

The Brigadier had been paying a visit of inspection to the Fort. During his walk round, a " three plus " air-raid developed and he stayed on to see the show. Before departing he made Don-Troop a present of his ideas, in the obliging way brigadiers have.

" The ammunition wasn't stacked as it should be . . ."

" There was too much shouting in the gun-pits . . ." And so on.

Later in the day, when the gunners had nothing better to do, they sat around the gun-pits criticising the criticisms.

" If we never get worse than that dose we'll be lucky," declared Smiler, the pleasant-faced bombardier on No. 3 gun, after a while. " As brigadiers go they might be regarded as compliments. Now if it had been old Chutney we'd have had something to chew on."

" What's Chutney doing now ? " inquired a gunner.

" Don't know. But if ever they send him to the Island it will be the blitz."

" Yes. He's hot stuff, all right," agreed the loader. " What an eye for detail, too ! . . . Misses nothing. I remember him years ago at Deepcut when he was battery commander. One day he was giving the battery a lecture on the buffer and recuperator. We all sat round on the grass in a ring and Chutney stood in the centre spouting it out. At the end of ten minutes he suddenly stopped and shot out his finger at about eight blokes, one after the other.

" ' You . . . you . . . you . . . you . . . See you get your boots mended at once,' he ordered.

" While he'd been talking he'd been making a mental note of all the blokes whose soles were wearing a bit thin."

" And I bet they didn't dare forget," added Smiler.

" Wonder if he's still the same since he became brigadier,"
said a gunner.

" Hotter than ever," the curly-headed bombardier assured
him. " I had a letter about him a few months ago from a
bombardier pal of mine who went out to France with the first
lot. His battery was up on the Franco-Belgian frontier.
My pal was promoted acting-sergeant. On the very next
day who should come along to inspect but old Chutney, as
you know, a brigadier now.

" ' Show me your aiming point, sergeant,' he raps out to
my pal.

" ' That church over there, sir.'

" ' What's the distance ? ' Chutney barks.

" My pal being a bit new to things, suddenly becomes
flustered, forgets the range, hesitates and tries to think,
instead of saying the first figure that comes into his head.
Chutney wouldn't have known any better. At least, there
was a chance. Finally my pal says :

" ' I forget, sir.'

" ' What's your rank ? ' asks Chutney.

" ' Sergeant, sir.'

" ' I mean your substantive rank.'

" ' Bombardier, sir,' replies my pal.

" From this afternoon you are a bombardier,' Chutney
informs him, and walks off.

" And so it was," concluded Smiler. " My pal was sergeant
for less than twenty-four hours."

" Chutney's all right once you get to know him," interposed
the lance-sergeant from the Command Post staff. " He's
keen as mustard himself, and you've got to be keen, too.
So long as you do things the way he wants them done you're
all right. I always found him a damn good bloke to his own
battery. He might give you a bawling-out himself, but he
wouldn't let anyone else butt in. Always stick up for you.
Very fair bloke, too, though strict."

In the general agreement the sergeant of No. 3 gun took
up the subject :

" I remember him first year I went out to India with an
18-pdr. battery. Chutney was our B.C. We were stationed
at Jubbelpore. That was round about 1930, in the days
when we were still horsed. You remember the rivalry that
existed over clean harness, and those inter-battery com-

petitions held to keep up the standard. Well, clean harness was Chutney's pet obsession. We used to spend all of a couple of days shining up for B.C.'s inspection after Church Parade. One Sunday my section went on parade not at all happy. The ammunition on the limbers had been sweating owing to the high temperature, and formed verdigris on the brass base of the shells. The verdigris rubbed off on to the leather cushions inside the limber flaps. We tried all ways to remove it. Scrubbing, scraping, metal polish . . . No good at all. So we knew we were for it. Along comes Chutney and first thing he spots is the verdigris.

" ' What the hell's the matter with this ? ' he shouts.

" ' We can't get it off, sir," says the section officer. ' We've tried our hardest.'

" ' What did you try ? '

" ' Everything, sir.'

" ' Everything but the right thing,' growls Chutney. ' I'll show you how to do it.'

" He turned to his native servant and spoke a few words to him which we didn't catch. The bloke walked off and Chutney went on with the inspection. Suddenly we saw the servant coming back across the square balancing a tray holding twelve glasses of lemonade. We all stared thunderstruck, wondering what the game was. The lemonade-wallah marched gravely up with the tray and halted behind Chutney who was bending over a gun and hadn't noticed him come up. After a bit he straightened himself up and turned round to discover what everybody was staring at. His face went purple when he saw that tray.

" ' You fool ! ' he blared. ' I said, fetch me twelve lemons. Not lemon squashes.'

" ' You can clean that verdigris off with lemon,' he snapped to the section officer, and pushed off bloody cross that he'd had his personal demonstration spoilt. Chutney always took pleasure in showing you himself where you'd gone wrong."

The stream of reminiscence concerning brigadiers, good, bad and indifferent, flowed on and on. On the outside edge of the group, stretched on his back, hands behind his head and tin-hat tilted forward over his face to keep off the sun, lay Lance-bombardier Doughy Baker, the solemn-countenanced youth who was a layer on No. 3 gun. He listened vaguely and without interest to the murmur of the conversation. Far from being entertained by it he found himself becoming more and more depressed. It was always the same with him whenever the members of the crew indulged in spells of reminiscence, as they frequently did. They talked of people and things and experiences which they had all shared in common during their long period of foreign service, and of which he knew nothing. On these occasions Doughy was conscious of feeling more than ever a sense of loneliness. Like being outside a very united family circle.

This had been the case ever since he joined the regiment in Malta as a replacement a year previously. He had made no friends in the Troop. The blame for this was not to be laid at the door of the gunners. They were well-disposed enough towards Doughy. But Doughy was a difficult subject for friendship though he hungered after it enough. He was by temperament reticent and slow in the uptake. You could tell so from a first glance at his stolid, heavy features. The Troop had christened him Doughy straight off because his name was Baker. But the nickname was far more appropriate than they guessed. In fact, it would not be doing him much injustice to describe him as half-baked. It was a fault, or rather a misfortune, with him that such ideas as he did possess were very slow in generating, and slower still in shaping themselves into speech. This failing reduced him to a state bordering upon the inarticulate. To Doughy both thinking and speaking were painful operations. So in company he made no headway at all. He was inclined to lapse into a brooding silence, and the conversation quickly left him far behind and out of sight altogether.

The Lance-bombardier was twenty-one, the youngest soldier in Don-Troop, many of whom were very old " sweats." He had never known his father or mother, and had been brought up in an orphanage. If he did possess any relatives he wasn't aware of it. He had always felt himself very much alone in the world. The year before war broke out found him a lift-attendant in a London hotel. He joined up, got a stripe on the strength of being reliable and conscientious in his duties, and left Woolwich for Malta early in 1940. It was on the troopship that he met Gunner Sharman who, like Doughy, was going out as a replacement to the 777th H.A.A. Regiment. Sharman resembled the Lance-bombardier in

27

being a quiet, non-talkative youth. An acquaintance sprang up between the pair which by the time they landed in Valetta had developed into friendship.

This was the first friend Doughy had ever possessed and the Lance-bombardier, being fully aware of his own short-comings as a companion, considered Sharman the best bit of luck that had ever come his way. The gunner's quiet, thoughtful style admirably suited the other's slow tempo. Sharman also had a knack of anticipating the half-fledged ideas that were floating about in Doughy's mind, before Doughy himself was fully aware of them. Which was an invaluable help in the case of a half-inarticulate comrade. Sometimes when they were wandering about Valetta together on a twenty-four hour pass it might vaguely cross Doughy's mind that it wouldn't be a bad idea to go to the pictures. Suddenly he would find himself following Sharman into a cinema without a word having passed. Sharman, too, seemed to understand and appreciate Doughy's frequent spells of silence. The pair would moon about the streets of Valetta for hours, barely exchanging six words, and return to their respective gun sites thinking how much they had enjoyed each other's company. All this suited Doughy as he had never been suited before.

Now he lay on his back outside the gun-pit staring into the inside of the tin-hat over his face, and seeing it as black as the future before him. Six weeks had passed since Sharman was killed on the Dockyard site in Malta's first air-raid. If possible, Doughy was feeling more conscious than ever of the tremendous crater that had been smashed into his daily existence by that fateful bomb. He saw himself faced with a resumption of the dreary loneliness and lack of human friendship that had always been his lot during the years before his meeting with Sharman. He had no hope of filling the gap. He would never find another Sharman. Sharman had understood him and appreciated him in a way nobody else was ever likely to. He knew only too well his own disadvantages.

Around him the gunners continued their resurrection of the past. More and more Doughy felt himself to be outside their little fraternity. His sense of loneliness deepened. He began to think that perhaps, after all, he'd better go into Valetta. Hitherto he had shunned the idea of walking about its streets and sitting in the cafés alone, where at every turn he would be reminded of the happy hours he had passed there with his dead friend. For five weeks he felt no inclination to leave the Fort. But the day previous he did put in for a twenty-four hours' pass. · It was in his pocket now, dated from 2 p.m. that day. After getting it he had changed his mind. And now he changed his mind again.

He jumped up from the ground, strode across to the dug-out and donned his khaki-drill trousers and topee. He descended the steps down the bastion to the little landing-stage at the base of the Fort. A *dghaisa*, Maltese cousin to a gondola, was rocking on the waters a foot or two from shore, maintained at that distance by the boatman with one of his long sweeps in accordance with the superstition that it is bad luck for a *dghaisa* ever to touch land. Doughy hopped aboard and was ferried across the harbour to Valetta.

It was late in the afternoon and the sun was still hot. Doughy wandered aimlessly up a side-street from the landing stage, across St. Paul's street and so into the Strada Stretta, one of Valetta's main avenues, in which thoroughfare were situated all the bars, cafés, cabarets, dance-halls and tattoo artists most patronised by the garrison. Here were " Auntie's " and " Rexfords," the cabarets popular among officers ; and " The Egyptian Queen," first choice with the men. At this hour of the afternoon, in the brilliant sunshine, the Strada Stretta presented an animated appearance. Troops from all the various units on the island—infantrymen, gunners and R.A.F. ground staff—thronged the pavements, mixed up with sailors from some destroyers in the Harbour, and Maltese civilians. Red-caps patrolled up and down in pairs. The buses were running again, and the horse-drawn *carrozins* (looking like four-poster beds on wheels), plied for hire by the kerbs.

It was towards " The Egyptian Queen " that Doughy's footsteps unconsciously led him. But at the entrance he remembered this was Sharman's favourite resort, and couldn't face it. He wandered on up the street jostled by the noisy, lively crowds. Outside the Continental Café, known to the troops as " The Gut," a Maltese tout with a terrific voice stood on the kerb whipping up custom. A specialist's knowledge of regimental badges, plus a quick eye enabled him to invest his soliciting with an individual appeal.

" Inside, Buffs. Big eats ! . . . Inside, Dorsets ! . . . Inside, Fusiliers. Big eats ! . . . " he bawled at the passing troops.

On catching sight of Doughy, he traversed to :

" Inside R.A. Big eats ! . . ."

Having nothing better to do but just to kill time Doughy entered a smallish room containing a dozen or so tables, a powerful smell of frying-oil, and a gabble of Maltese chatter from behind a couple of tea-urns. He ordered fried eggs with chips and tomatoes, fruit salad, and tea. He dallied there for some time, mechanically glancing through a much-stained copy of the *Times of Malta*. Then he paid his bill with a half-crown note and returned to the sunlight, mournfully thinking how different the fried eggs and chips would have tasted had Sharman been there.

After letting himself be carried along listlessly by the crowds for a while he drifted into a club called " La Valette," run by a Maltese. Here a non-stop tombola game, otherwise known as " housey-housey," was in full swing. A large hall, hazy with cigarette smoke was dotted with small tables at which dozens of soldiers and Maltese civilians sat drinking. In one corner was a bar, and three-quarters of the way up the room was a clear space with a raised platform. Here, on a stool with a high desk in front of him sat the " shouter " with a big board divided into·squares, each square containing a number, from one to ninety-nine.

Doughy went up to the bar and bought himself a drink and a couple of threepenny tombola tickets. These were divided into fifteen squares, each bearing a different number. He wandered into the hall and sat down at a table opposite a corporal in the Hampshires.

A new session was just beginning. The Maltese " shouter " on the platform took hold of a wicker basket shaped like a big onion and shook it vigorously. Then he turned it upside down and out of the narrow neck dropped a thick round disc bearing a number.

" Twenty-seven," he shouted, and placed the disc on the appropriate square on the board in front of him.

All over the room the players scanned their tickets to see if they contained number 27. Those who had it ticked it off, the eventual winner being the man whose fifteen numbers turned up first.

30

The " shouter " continued to shake the bottle and bawl out the numbers.  As the tickets began to fill up the excitement increased and the conversation throughout the hall died away.  So far Doughy had had poor luck.  Only two of his numbers had turned up.

" Eighty - two . . . Four . . . Fifty-seven . . ." the " shouter " announced as the discs dropped in turn out of the basket.  Sometimes he varied the procedure by shouting out, instead of the numbers themselves, their slang equivalents, all of these being quite familiar to the habitués of the game.

" Top of the house (99) . . . Gertie Leigh (33) . . . Dinkey-Doo (22) . . . Kelly's eye (1) . . ."

After the session had lasted ten minutes the corporal at Doughy's table hoarsely whispered :

" How are you filling ? "

" No good.  Six," replied Doughy.

" I only want one more," said the corporal, breathing heavily.  " And haven't I got a sweat on . . ."

The perspiration was, in fact, noticeable on his forehead ; partly due to the heat of the hall, partly to the feelings engendered by proximity to success.

" Doctor's shop (9) . . ." bawled the " shouter."

The corporal took an excited leap to his feet.

" House ! " he yelled, to the accompaniment of groans from the other players in the room who had been on the verge of filling.

Pushing his way to the platform in the centre of the room, the corporal had his card checked up from the discs on the numbered board, and received the winner's dividend on that " house."

" Not so bad," he informed Doughy when he returned. " Four pounds, seventeen . . . Have another ' Blue ' with me ? "

Doughy declined the drink.  He had vaguely hoped that the excitement of the tombola game might take his mind off Sharman for a bit.  But it hadn't worked.  It wouldn't have worked even if he had been a winner.  He'd never have ' got a sweat on ' . . . He finished his Blue Label and quitted the hall in search of some more promising distraction. Finally, after sauntering up and down the Strada Stretta till it was getting dark, lonely among all the bustle and life around him, he passed through the swing doors of the Balmoral.

The Balmoral was a popular dance-hall with a large floor and plenty of tables round the edges. Its colour scheme was blue and silver, and the walls were lavishly panelled with gilt-framed mirrors. A bar had been installed in a side-room leading off from the hall, and when Doughy entered this was packed so tight with soldiers and sailors drinking that there was hardly room to move. The dance floor was pretty crowded too. Some of the troops were dancing with girls they had brought in from outside. Others were going round with the dance-partners belonging to the establishment. There were about a couple of dozen of these girls to suit all tastes, some youngish, others not so young, some plump, some thin, most of them dark, but here and there a blonde or two. They worked on a commission basis. When you bought a girl a drink the waiter gave her a check and she got a percentage back at the end of the night. While waiting to be hired by clients the girls parked at tables by themselves in one corner of the dance-hall.

Doughy seated himself with a beer at a vacant table not far away. The Maltese orchestra on the platform at the end of the room was punching out a fox-trot. A one-step followed. Then another fox-trot. These were the favourite dances of the assembly. Doughy sat for some time, sipping his beer, idly watching the couples on the floor shaking themselves about. Occasionally a disengaged dance-partner looked across at him and smiled. But it meant nothing to Doughy. He didn't know how to dance. In any case, he had only entered the hall because he had to go somewhere, and the Balmoral possessed the merit of being a place where he had never been with Sharman. So there wouldn't be any memories. . . .

Suddenly, towards the end of a rumba, a row developed between a couple of infantrymen. Doughy did not know the cause but it appeared to have something to do with one of the dance-partners, a young Maltese girl in a pink, artificial silk frock, and black shoes and stockings. Voices rose high, a table was knocked over, and there was a crash of glasses. Taking no chances of a rough house the proprietor of the hall darted through the swing-doors into the street. He returned in a few moments with a couple of military police.

The red-caps wasted no time on pros and cons.  Each took hold of one of the infantrymen by the arm.

" Come along, boys.  You'll feel better in the fresh air," they said, steering the two men into the street, where they despatched them upon their different ways.

The excitement subsided and the dancing was resumed. Doughy growing gloomier and gloomier made up his mind every minute to clear out.  But nearly an hour passed and he was still there.

In the middle of the mixture of music, scraping of ammunition-boots on the dance floor and the loud hum of conversation from the packed bar the Maltese attendant at the swing-doors darted into the hall.

" Air-raid . . ." he yelled.

Nobody took much notice.  The band continued playing. A few nervous girls stopped dancing and hurried out, escorted by their partners.  Soon the guns could be heard firing, and occasionally the explosion of a bomb.

After twenty minutes the bombs began to drop nearer. The management decided it was time to close down and seek safety in a shelter.  The band packed up and everyone filed out into the deserted Strada Stretta.

It was a very dark night without a trace of moon or stars. Having nowhere in particular to go Doughy picked his way for a while along the Strada Stretta and then branched off up a side street.  Not a soul was to be seen.  Nearing the top he stood for a moment or two watching the shells bursting round a three-engined bomber caught in the beams of four searchlights.  Suddenly there was a prolonged whine followed by a loud explosion.  The blast from the bomb whipped round the corner of the street and flung Doughy against the wall of a house.  He could hear the wreckage of buildings falling not far away.  Looking around he saw a figure lying in the road only a few yards behind him.  He hurried back to it.

It was the Maltese dance girl who had been involved in the altercation between the two soldiers.  He recognised her at once by the pink frock.

" You hurt ? " he asked, lifting her to her feet.

She wasn't.  Only half-dead with fright.  She clung to his arm, shaking violently.

"No need for you to be scared," he said.  "You're all right."

C                                  33

She shook her head. " I not brave," she gasped. " Not like you. You brave."

She clutched his arm tighter still. Doughy was far too modest to pretend to any undue degree of fearlessness. Still, if it were any comfort to the trembling girl to think he was brave she might as well have it. So he compromised by saying :

" Oh, well, you see. I'm a soldier," as though that fact explained a lot.

" You don't want to let yourself be frightened by noise," he continued, hoping to steady her. " Bombs are more'n three-quarters noise. You want to get in the habit of following 'em as they come down. So long as you hear them you know you're safe. Listen . . . Here comes another. Hear it ? . . . hear it ? . . .",

A bomb whined down and exploded some distance away. It was near enough, nevertheless, to start the girl shivering again.

" I not like it," she cried, agitatedly. " I go home quick. Always. When the bombs."

" Where do you live ? "

" In the shelter."

" I'll see you on your way," said Doughy.

Clutching at his arm in her fear, she led him through several streets till they went down one with a bastion at the corner. From here one could look out across the harbour. With a refreshing breeze blowing against his face from the sea Doughy lingered for a few moments watching the distant flashes of the guns on the Fort Pedro site as they tore red holes in the darkness.

" They're our 3.7's," he said, pointing towards the flashes.

The girl neither understood nor cared. All she wanted at that moment was to get underground. The entrance to the air-raid shelter was between two buildings near the end of the street. Outside was a small shrine cut out of the lime-stone rock and containing a coloured and gilded plaster statue of the Virgin and Child. Two tiny oil lamps burned within the niche in front of it.

The girl slipped round the blast wall at the entrance to the shelter and disappeared. She disappeared just as swiftly from Doughy's mind. By the time he had walked back on to the bastion he had forgotten all about her. Once more he stood there watching the red flashes of the Pedro guns. He was thinking he'd have done far better if he'd stayed on the gun-site. His leave-pass had been a failure. He couldn't have been more conscious there of his loneliness than he had been in Valetta, haunted all the time by the ghost of Sharman.

Depressed and deflated, he returned to the Strada Stretta to look for a sleeping - house. He stopped before one with a board over the door on which was chalked the information :

" NO BUGS . . . NO FLEAS . . . CLEAN BED . . . 1/6."

He handed over his one-and-sixpence to the Maltese at the door.

" Call me at eight," he said.

" All called same time," was the terse reply. " Like tea ? "

" Yes."

" Twopence extra."

Doughy climbed up a flight of stairs to a big blacked-out room containing over a dozen iron bedsteads ranged along the walls. Most of them were already occupied by sleepers. The room, miserably illuminated by small oil lamps made from old metal polish tins, smelt of beer fumes and paraffin.

He sat on the side of his bed and began to undress. Suddenly the sleeper next to him uttered a frantic yell, flung back the bed-clothes and leaped half naked on to the floor. It was so unexpected that Doughy also sprang to his feet.

" Sorry if I startled you, mate," the soldier apologised, with a grin. " I ain't suddenly been taken barmy. I just got out to make room for this flea."

## IV—Reduced to the Ranks

THE second air-raid of the morning had just ended. Over Valetta and the three cities, Vittoriosa, Cospicua and Senglea, on the south side of Grand Harbour, half-a-dozen separate clouds of yellowish dust from wrecked buildings still hung, slowly dissipating in the slight breeze. At Fort Pedro Don-

Troop was taking advantage of the lull to clean its guns, an operation already once interrupted.

Sweating, grimy and stripped to the waist, in No. 3 gun-pit Smiler, Doughy and Steve Jordan, the loader, were scrubbing out the interior of the bore of their 3.7 with a long-handled stiff-bristled piassaba brush, having first closed the breech with an empty cartridge-case, and poured buckets of hot water down the muzzle. Together the three of them tugged, thrust, and twisted the brush. Not easy work, even then.

" I think we've done enough," said Steve, at the end of half an hour, fingering the rifling of the gun to make sure it was clean.

" We have," replied Smiler decisively. It's twelve o'clock. We got to smart ourselves up for the reception yet. That'll take a bit of time."

For a moment or two he watched the solemn-faced Doughy in the act of removing the empty cartridge-case from the breech.

" You come along with us to the reception, Doughy," he suggested. " Cheer you up. Help you to forget. There's sure to be lots to drink. And lots of skirt."

" I'm told there'll be champagne," said Steve.

Doughy understood. It was the first time Smiler or Steve had invited him to share their pleasures. They knew he was feeling lonely without Sharman. He thought it kind of them but was not enthusiastic. It wouldn't be like going out with Sharman.

" I haven't had an invite," he said.

" You don't want an invite," replied Smiler, contempt-uously. " The more of us that turn up the better José'll like it. Make all his relatives think he really is R.A. Besides, you can go in place of Honesty. His heart for weddings 's been knocked clean out of him by what happened yesterday. And I don't blame him."

José was a Maltese cook at the Fort. He belonged to the Malta Auxiliaries which supplied men for work in the cook-house, thus releasing gunners for more essential duties. As Smiler had said, he was very proud of his connection with the Army, and had been lavish with invitations to gunners of the troop for the reception to follow his wedding in Floriana at twelve mid-day. A slight shadow had been cast over the proceedings by an unfortunate incident on the previous day. The butcher of the troop, also a loader, was a powerful giant of a man universally known as " Honesty " because that, apart from his muscles, was his outstanding characteristic. He was so honest that he declined to draw his trade pay as a butcher because the duties took up so little of his time. The Troop considered that proof of honesty could go no further.

On the previous afternoon José happened to be passing when Honesty was cutting up the meat ration. Burning with anxiety to please his soldier guests at the reception next day, and afraid lest they might not appreciate the Maltese dishes, José ventured to suggest that Honesty should cut him off a piece of beef that he could take home and get cooked for them. There being at the time no shortage of meat Honesty, without thinking much about the matter, agreed. José departed from the Fort with the meat under his arm, was stopped not far away by two detectives, cross-examined, and escorted back to the Fort.

As a sequel the astounded butcher, with whom honesty had been the guiding principle of his life, was informed by the Regimental Sergeant-Major that he would be going before the Battery Commander. He was now awaiting the interview, heavily depressed by the thought that he of all people should be suspected of " flogging the rations," and wondering what was going to happen to him. No wonder, as Smiler said, he had no heart at the moment for wedding receptions. Above all for José's.

" I haven't got a leave pass," said Doughy, glad to think of another chance of escaping the invitation.

Smiler and Steve were each in happy possession of the usual twenty-four hours' pass which the men got on an average once a fortnight.

" Burtenshaw will stand-in for you," replied Smiler, brushing aside the objection. " He was going to stand-in for Honesty. You ask him. He won't mind. And you can easily square sergeant. He likes you."

Doughy departed, against his better wishes, to find Gunner Burtenshaw.

Punctually at twelve-thirty, the time on their passes, the three of them passed through the gate of the Fort. In honour of the occasion they had arrayed themselves in khaki-drill trousers, shirts, ammunition boots, and tropical khaki topees with the Gunner red-and-blue flash on the side of the crown.

" We don't want to dirty our boots," said Steve.

A little way along the road they were lucky enough to meet a *carrozin.* They climbed in and gave the driver the address.

He grinned and nodded understandingly. " Yés, yes. José's wedding."

" Whatever this bloke José does makes a noise," commented Smiler.

" We might make him pay for this cab," suggested Steve. " It's his wedding, not ours."

On arriving at the house in the Floriana district of Valetta they entered a good-sized room the walls of which were spattered with fancy mirrors of all shapes and sizes, in shell and coral frames. There were mirrors in the backs of the china cabinets, and the mantelpiece glittered with glass ornaments.

" What's this ?  The Crystal Palace ? " murmured Smiler.

In the centre of the room, clad in her white satin bridal dress with a long train, the bride, a pretty girl with intensely black hair, and intensely black, merry eyes, stood receiving the noisy felicitations of a crowd of Maltese relatives and guests, many of them workers at the Dockyard where her father was a foreman. The men were all dressed alike in black clothes and white buttonholes. The black dresses of the elderly female guests also suggested a funeral rather than a wedding, but the younger ones wore bright-coloured summer frocks. Smiler was more interested in noting that everyone in the room except himself and his friends was holding a well-filled glass. Through an open doorway he noticed an inner room where stood a well-filled buffet laden with trays of Maltese dishes and bottles of wine and beer.

José, also attired in black, welcomed the soldiers with a shout of delight, and proudly led them forward to be introduced to the bride. The crowd made way for them, as for honoured guests. At first sight, the bride recalled to Doughy the girl he had met on the night of the air-raid. But next moment he saw there was no real resemblance.

" We're dying to drink her health, José," said Smiler.

Beaming with pleasure José ushered them into the buffet where his brother, the proprietor of a local café, presided over the liberal spread, his own personal contribution to the festivities.

" Ah, you want the champagne ? " he grinned.

" That'll do to begin with," replied Steve.

Smiler ran his eye over the bottles on the buffet with approval. Besides champagne there was sherry, port, Chianti, gin and bitters, and a pleasing sufficiency of the bottled beer known simply as Blue Label and, simpler still, " Blue."

" Have as much of them as you like, Doughy," he said. " But keep off that Ambeet." He indicated a couple of bottles of a brownish concoction peculiar to Malta. " It's dynamite," he added. " You don't feel so bad on it for a time, but when you wake up next morning it's got you blotto. Like a delayed-action bomb. Anything else but that, Doughy, as you're not much used to drinking."

Doughy thanked him for the advice. The three gunners stood in the doorway drinking, and occasionally lifting their glasses in the direction of the bride. Some guests departed, but more arrived to take their places. The pop of champagne corks punctuated the chatter and laughter that filled the room as the party gathered way. Doughy, who had never known what it was to have relatives of his own, studied the crowd of uncles and aunts and cousins oscillating around José and his bride, with a mournful interest. He tried to convince himself that he was glad he had come, and was enjoying himself. But despite the champagne, every now and then he felt himself alone and thinking of Sharman.

After a while a little orchestra appeared, violin, guitar, drum, saxophone, and piano-accordion. They ensconced themselves in a corner of the room and commenced to play dance music. As soon as the couples began to move Smiler noticed that three Maltese girls, sitting on the far side of the room, were casting glances in their direction.

" We're wanted over there, Steve," he said.

They joined the three interested girls.

" I'm Smiler. This is Steve and Doughy," said Smiler, by way of introduction. " What are your names ? "

They were Josephine, Maria and Tesa.

" Fine. We'll all have a dance. Brisk up, Doughy."

" I can't dance," said Doughy.

" Then hold on to Tesa while she does."

After a spell of dancing on the stone-tiled floor the guests needed rest and refreshment. The bride's father rose and made an announcement in Maltese that was greeted with applause.

"Anything we ought not to know ?" asked Smiler.

The girls explained that the little ones, the bride's nephews and nieces, were going to sing a Maltese folk-song. Four small girls and a boy stepped into the centre of the room and started singing, accompanied by the piano-accordion. At the conclusion of the song the guests clapped vigourously, and the children sang one or two more.

"Your go now, Steve," said Smiler. "Show 'em what the Army can do."

One of the Maltese girls stood up and announced to the company : " The Tommy is going to sing one England native hymn," and in a throaty baritone, Steve delivered himself of "Danny Boy". This went down so well that he obliged with a second " native hymn " entitled " Two Little Girls in Blue," which proved even more successful. Even Doughy appreciated it. He found its dreary theme in tune with his own mood.

More dancing followed. The afternoon wore on and as the reception was to be continued throughout the night Smiler suggested to the three girls that they should all go to the pictures to make a break. The cinema was only a quarter of an hour's walk, but before they reached it the air-raid warning sirens commenced to wail. Smiler and Steve wanted to go on to the cinema. The girls were nervous and wanted to go to an air-raid shelter. Doughy didn't care where he went.

In the end it was arranged that Smiler and Doughy should escort the girls to the shelter while Steve went to the cinema and bought the tickets, to save time later on. When the raid was over and Smiler and his party arrived at the cinema there was no sign of Steve. They waited in vain outside for some time.

"I'll bet he's found something else and gone off, leaving us to pay for the three," Smiler said to Doughy, indignantly.

They took seats in the circle. A picture was in the middle of showing. In the dim light Smiler suddenly focussed his eyes upon a bald patch on the top of a head four rows in front. He nudged Doughy.

"See . . . Steve. Now watch."

He chewed up the end of a cigarette packet into small pellets and started to flick them at the bald patch in front of him. The recipient of these favours began to pat himself smartly on the scalp, thinking it was flies. Each time he did so, Josephine, Maria and Tesa giggled with delight. Once the head in front half-turned round with an irritated gesture. The girls thought it funnier than the Marx Brothers. So did Smiler. Doughy was thinking of the last time he had been to the pictures with Sharman.

At length came the interval and the lights went up. The bald-patched head leisurely turned to look behind.

" Blimey . . . The Brigadier, . . ." ejaculated Smiler. " Get down, Doughy."

For the rest of the interval they crouched down in their seats, hiding their faces and praying to escape detection. The three girls thought this was the funniest part of the lot.

" You enjoy yourselves much louder and we'll be for it," hissed Smiler from his place of concealment.

Then the lights went down again and he emerged with a sigh of relief.

When they returned to the reception Steve was already awaiting them.

" Where did you get to ? " demanded Smiler.

" I met an old friend."

" I guessed so," said Smiler, disgustedly.  " What was wrong with our three ?  One Maltese girl is as good as another, isn't she ? "

" Mine was English," vouchsafed Steve, a trifle loftily.

" Oh," said Smiler, mollified, accepting the explanation as fully satisfactory.

More dancing, more refreshment, and more again. The reception carried on into the night. From time to time the bride, under her olive skin, acquired a greenish, sickly pallor and began to sway ominously. Whereupon, understanding matrons attended her upstairs whence she returned after an hour or so, fresh and composed again, to give a new fillip to the party. Josephine, Maria and Tesa suffered under no such disabilities. Much to the admiration of Smiler and Steve they took all that was given them without turning a hair. Just as their spirits rose higher and higher those of Doughy sank lower and lower. Vainly he waited for the cheering-up process to begin, as prophesied by Smiler. All that happened

was that the hours seemed to become heavier. At last, in
the small part of the morning, the reception died away.
José and his bride had long since disappeared, the orchestra
had gone, and most of the guests had departed to their own
homes. There remained only the three gunners and a few
members of the family. These distributed themselves on
sofas and easy chairs and dropped off into heavy slumbers.

At half-past nine another air-raid aroused them all to the
more commonplace side of daily existence.

" I got three heads." groaned Smiler, smoothing-out some
of the creases in his battle-dress.

" I know a bar that shouldn't be open but is," said Steve.
" We'll go along and have a livener."

Accompanied by an unsteady and preoccupied Doughy
they quitted the house and made their way to the bar in
the Dockyard area, where they summoned up the recuperative
powers of several Blue Labels.

At last Smiler announced it was time they were getting
back to the Fort.

" I'm on guard at two," he said. " And I've got to
spruce up."

Steve followed him to the door. Doughy remained where
he sat.

" Come on, Doughy. We're going now," called Smiler.

" You go to hell," suddenly shouted Doughy in a thick
voice. " I'm stopping here."

Smiler returned to the table. " Come along with us,
Doughy," he said firmly. " It's eleven now, and you've got
to be back by twelve-thirty."

" I'm going back when I want to."

" You bloody fool . . ." exclaimed Smiler. " You been
drinking that ambeet after I told you what it would do to you
next morning. You're coming back to the Fort."

He caught hold of Doughy's arm and was roughly shaken
off. For some minutes he stood over him, trying to persuade
him to return to the Fort with them, and emphasising the
troubles in store for him if he overstayed his leave. Suddenly
Doughy half-rose from his seat and dealt him a blow in the
chest that sent him staggering backwards to the door.

" All right," shouted Smiler angrily. " Have it your own
way. My motto is, let bloody fools be bloody fools."

He departed into the street.

" Sonny," Steve warned the bar-keeper before he followed, " see you don't serve that soldier any, or to-morrow you won't be opening as early as usual."

That afternoon there was a decided atmosphere of discomfort in No. 3 gun-pit, and it was not due to air-raids. Doughy's absence was the cause. The sergeant was in a fuming temper. He bitterly resented being let down, most of all by Doughy.

" Last time ever I go out of my way to do any of you a favour," he swore. " I wouldn't have been surprised if any of the others had let me down. But I'd have sworn I could trust Doughy."

But the sergeant's temper was as nothing compared with that of the gunner who had stood-in for the absentee. He had a date that afternoon to take a girl to the pictures in Valetta. At the thought of her waiting in vain outside the cinema he filled the gun-pit with imprecations on Doughy.

Steve also experienced an uncomfortable time. In the absence of the real culprit both the sergeant and the stand-in persisted in blaming him for what had happened, which he considered most unwarrantable, especially as he had carefully remained silent as to the exact facts of the affair. He heartily envied Smiler, on guard at the gate, and clear of all the fuss.

Towards five o'clock one of the limber-gunners who was off duty slid into the pit and whispered a few words to Steve. His face lengthened. He walked over to the aggrieved stand-in.

" Just had the wire from Smiler on the gate," he muttered. " Doughy's in the clink. Brought in by a couple of red-caps. Close arrest, I hear. They put handcuffs on him."

" Serve the bastard right," was the response. " I wish they'd put a ring through his nose, too."

In the hot Battery Office the Battery Sergeant-major sat making out Doughy's crime sheet.

'" Lance-bombardier Henry Baker, No. 506602, charged under Sect. 15, Par. 2 of the Army Act with overstaying leave from 12.30 p.m. Thursday till 4.30 p.m. Thursday, August 27, 1940. Also charged under Sect. 22, Par 3 of the Army Act with resisting arrest. Also charged under Sect. 40 Par. 2, with conduct prejudicial to good order and discipline.'

The crime sheet, apart from its present specific purpose,

43

was the Army form upon which a man's case-history is entered from the day of his joining the Regiment. Doughy's form up till now was a nice, clean blank except for the record of his promotion to lance-bombardier. As the Sergeant-Major took the sheet in to the Battery Commander it puzzled him to imagine how such a well-behaved, conscientious chap as Doughy came to be in such a mess.

" I'll see him at once," said the Battery Commander.

In a few minutes the tramp, tramp of Doughy and his escort sounded outside.

" Prisoner and escort . . . Halt ! " came the voice of the B.S.M.

The door of the office was flung open.

" Cap off ! . . . Prisoner and escort . . . Quick march. . . Ri-wheel . . . Lef-wheel . . . Halt ! . . . Ri-turn ! . . ."

This manœuvre brought a flushed and sullen-looking Doughy facing the Major at his trestle table.

The Battery-Commander read the charge :

" You are Lance-bombardier Henry Baker, No. 506602 (to which Doughy mechanically replied : ' Yes, sir ', twice). You are charged under Section . . ." etc., etc. " Anything to say ? "

" No, sir."

" I must confess," observed the Battery Commander, after a brief pause, " that I'm surprised to find a man of your good character in such a serious position. What happened ? "

There was no reply. Only an obstinate tightening of Doughy's jaw. The Battery Commander recognised the symptoms. He was far too experienced to waste further time.

" Whom did you spend your leave with ? " he asked.

Doughy gave the names of Smiler and Steve.

" Warn both of them for witnesses in case they're needed," the Battery Commander informed the Sergeant-Major. He addressed Doughy again : " I shan't be able to deal with this case. I'll have to remand you for the Colonel."

And Doughy was escorted back to the guard-room near the entrance to the Fort.

An air-raid was in full blast when the fate of Doughy was being decided before the Colonel during the middle of the following morning. The continuous roar of the guns of the Fort, engaged in their tremendous mechanistic drama outside, shook the foundations of the office and seemed to mock the petty little human drama inside with its own insignificance.

The two military policemen told how they had come across Doughy in a street in Valetta, asked to see his pass and found that he had overstayed his leave. He was also drunk. He had resisted arrest by shaking his arms free.

Smiler and Steve gave their evidence.

" What about this reception ? " asked the Colonel.

" A very quiet affair, sir," Smiler assured him. " It had to be, sir. Recent mourning in the family, I think. Most of the guests wore black."

" Were you three sober when you left the house ? "

" Perfectly, sir. If I may say so, sir, I think the lance-bombardier must have got a touch of the sun. I noticed he wasn't looking very well."

The Colonel listened to it all unimpressed.

" I don't admire the conduct of you two, deserting a comrade in this way," he said, severely.

" We did all we could, sir. Short of carrying him back," protested Smiler in an injured tone.

" That's enough. You can go," said the Colonel.

He turned to Doughy. " Anything to say ? "

" No sir," replied Doughy stolidly. He was no longer flushed, and his features had regained their normal serious cast.

The Battery Commander interposed :

" I'd like, sir, to put it on record that he is a man of excellent character, sober, and most conscientious. It is a mystery to me what can have come over him."

" Why were you so foolish as to resist arrest ? " the Colonel asked Doughy.

" I didn't want to be touched, sir."

" Didn't want to be touched," exclaimed the Colonel. " That's no explanation."

" I wanted to be left alone, sir."

" Why ? " the Colonel asked, puzzled.

" Don't know, sir . . . That's how I felt," Doughy stated simply.

He forbore to mention that the drink, instead of drowning his sorrows, had floated them to the surface again with increased sharpness ; and that he had bitterly resented any intrusion between himself and his aching longing for the

45

dead Sharman.   What was the use of saying that, he thought.
It wouldn't be understood.   He couldn't quite understand
it himself.

" This is a very serious matter," began the Colonel gravely,
after a pause.   " Absent from leave . . . resisting arrest . . .
drunk . . . In war time, too.   You were given your stripe
as being a man fitted to assume responsibility.   You have
shown yourself, by your recent behaviour, to be unfitted.
I have no option but to sentence you to fourteen days detention, and to be reduced to the rank of gunner."

He waited for a few moments and then proceeded :

" Are you willing to accept my verdict, or do you wish to
take a court-martial ? "

" I'll take your verdict, sir," said Doughy.

The Regimental Sergeant-Major sprang to life :

" Prisoner and escort . . . Ri-turn . . . Quick march . . .
Ri-wheel . . ."

Boom . . . Boom . . . Boom . . . Boom . . . The guns
continued to thunder.


V—Gunner on Reconnaissance

At the end of a fortnight an escort from the Fort collected
Gunner Doughy Baker at the gates of the detention barracks
and deposited him safe and sound on the gun-site, there to
resume his interrupted career as layer on No. 3 gun.   To all
outward appearance he was, except for being minus his
stripe, the same stolid, serious-faced Doughy as ever.

On the first opportunity Smiler and Steve drew him aside.

" No ill-feeling, I hope, Doughy ? " remarked Smiler
briskly.

" Ill-feeling ?   Why ? " asked Doughy, slightly puzzled.

" That's all right then," said Smiler, relieved ;   " You
can't say we didn't do our best to bring you back to the Fort
with us.   Don't you take any notice of what the C.O. said
about us deserting a comrade.   That don't mean anything.
He's got to exaggerate on them occasions just to look stern.
It was hard on me and Steve, but we've got over it now."

" You didn't desert me no more than I deserted you,"
said Doughy, simply.

46

" As for that stripe you lost," continued Smiler. " Well, what's a dog's leg anyhow ? I've got two of 'em, and am I any better off ? What's a bob or two, anyway. The only one who benefits is my wife who I haven't seen for six years and don't want to see for another six."

" I'm not sore about the stripe," said Doughy.

" That bar-keeper serve you after we left ? " asked Steve.

" No."

" Lucky for him. How did you get on in clink ? "

" All right."

" Food good ? "

" Good enough."

" I see you got sense, Doughy," said Smiler, approvingly. " Clink's whatever you like to make it. And that's a fact some blokes never learn. How did you amuse yourself ? "

" Thinking a bit."

" What about ? "

" Myself."

" I see you did have a dull time," said Steve.

But Doughy's thoughts during detention had been to him anything but of a dull nature. He had, after much deliberation, arrived at a decision that stirred his sluggish temperament into a ferment. Smiler and Steve saw no visible change in their comrade. But behind Doughy's usual stolid, inanimate exterior glowed the fire of a new purpose.

The spark had been lit on his second night in the detention barracks, when he had been feeling very miserable and lonely and, as usual, had commenced to dwell on the blankness of the future now that his one friend and confidant Sharman was no more. He despaired of ever finding another like Sharman.

Doughy understood that he wasn't made for friendship on the ordinary plane such as existed between other gunners at the Fort, between Steve and Smiler for instance. All that quick, easy talk, that rapid transit from one topic to another, that ready communicativeness, was, he knew, beyond him. And he was fully aware it was such things that gave the average friendship a start and kept it going afterwards. With Sharman it had been different. He had never met anyone else like Sharman. He would never again meet anyone like Sharman.

And then, without knowing why, Doughy found himself

thinking of José's wedding. It was the first time it had entered his head since the door of the house in Floriana closed behind him on the morning after the reception. And now he had a distinct picture before him of José standing in the glass-decked room crowded with wedding guests and watching his bride, the little dark, beady-eyed Maltese girl who, at first sight, had reminded Doughy of the girl he had escorted to the air-raid shelter on his first leave in Valetta without Sharman. What is more, he had a distinct picture of the confidential glances exchanged between José and his bride now and again across the distance of the room. Doughy remembered noticing these glances at the time. The pair had just looked at one another for an instant, and then seemed to know exactly what was in each other's minds. They didn't have to speak a word.

" Just like me and Sharman used to," thought Doughy, sadly.

That night he went to sleep envying José, and thinking of the vague resemblance between José's bride and the Maltese girl he had met on the night of the air-raid.

Next day Doughy found himself dwelling more and more on this fleeting likeness. Then, as time went on, José's bride receded into the background and he thought of the other girl by herself alone. He hadn't a very clear picture of her to work on. He had been so uninterested in her at the first meeting that he could hardly remember her features. He was sorry he hadn't taken more notice of them when he had the chance. But he did remember her black eyes, and that expression on her face, something similar to the one he had observed on the face of José's bride when she and her new husband exchanged their understanding glances. Doughy began to wonder what she was doing now, and what her name was.

" Clink," all the world over, has this advantage, that it provides a man with good opportunities for concentrated thought about himself. The more Doughy thought, the firmer became his conviction that in the unknown black-eyed Maltese girl he might find a suitable successor to the lamented Sharman. It was the first time in his life he had ever thought about a girl in this way, as a friend and confidant. If it hadn't been for noticing the close understanding, independent of words, that seemed to exist between José and his bride, and that reminded him so much of himself and Sharman, the idea would never have entered his head now. He had always connected girls with lots of talk and conversation, the very things he was so deficient in.

By the end of one week he had made up his mind. At the first opportunity he would go to Valetta and have a look round for the Maltese girl. Having once decided on this he allowed nothing to weaken his determination. Not even his dread of looking ridiculous. Which was big. Not even his lurking suspicion that he could never really replace Sharman. Which was bigger.

He had been back on the gun-site for nearly three weeks before his turn for a twenty-four hours pass came round.

" You mind your step, Doughy," warned Smiler, on seeing him tidying himself up to go into Valetta. " You won't have me and Steve to look after you this time. Mind you keep off the drink. . . . It's poison to you."

" He can't lose his dog's leg again, whatever happens," said Steve cheerfully.

" Don't listen to him, Doughy. How're you going to pass the time ? "

" Have a walk round. Have some eats. Go to the pictures," replied Doughy, fastening his battle-blouse.

" Sounds safe enough," said Smiler. " You stick to that, Doughy, and you'll be all right. And keep out of The Grotto. Or you'll need four red-caps to see you home."

Doughy crossed the Harbour in a *dghaisa*. His leave pass extended from 2 p.m. till the same time next day. It was now three o'clock, a gloriously sunny afternoon, and he felt that with ample time in front of him there was no need to hurry. Shortly after he stepped off the landing-stage at Valetta the sirens began to wail. In a brief while the streets were deserted. The guns of the defence began to roar and he stood for a moment or two trying to see if he could distinguish the sound of his own 3.7's on Fort Pedro. Then bombs began to fall from three or four Italian planes flying over fifteen thousand feet up. Most of them dropped harmlessly in the sea well outside the harbour, but one or two fell in the Dockyard area, near enough for Doughy to take cover under an archway. The raid was soon over and, with the brilliant atmosphere a bit dimmed by the clouds of limestone dust from newly-wrecked buildings, he proceeded to make

his way to the Strada Stretta. He had formulated no plans
of action beyond going to the Balmoral, the café where he
had first seen the girl whose existence now seemed so vital
to him, in the hope that he would find her there.

As he proceeded along the Strada Stretta his determination
wilted a little. He felt a relief that the doors of Balmoral
wouldn't be open yet. He turned into an eats house and
lingered over a plate of fish and chips and some tea. Afterwards, still feeling there was no need to hurry the business,
he took himself to the pictures.

Dusk had fallen when he left the cinema and made his
way with dogged resolution to the Balmoral. The little
orchestra was already hard at work, although only three
couples occupied the floor of the blue and silver dance hall.
But the adjacent bar was busy enough, packed with thirsty
troops of all denominations. Doughy slid inside and sat
down at one of the unoccupied side-tables. After a few
seconds his eyes began to move around cautiously in search
of the Maltese girl. She was nowhere to be seen, neither
among the dancers nor among the vacant partners. It was
a disappointment and a relief combined. He conquered the
temptation to walk out at once, and settled down on the
off-chance that she might show up later.

A thin-faced girl with a beaky nose suddenly dropped into
the vacant seat at his table.

" You dance with me ? " she inquired.

Doughy mumbled that he didn't dance.

" You buy me a drink ? " she persisted in a friendly
manner.

An obliging waiter had already taken his stand at
Doughy's elbow. He bought the girl a sherry, and a Blue
Label for himself. An uncomfortable minute or two passed
in silence. Finally it occurred to Doughy he might as well
make his companion earn her drink. Rehearsing in his
mind the words to say, and putting on as casual a tone as
possible, he gave a sketchy description of the girl he was in
search of and inquired where she was that evening.

The beaky-nosed dance partner seemed to understand at
last whom he meant.

" She no longer work here," she said.

" Where's she gone ? "

His companion shrugged high a pair of indifferent shoulders, to denote that the present location of her former colleague was a matter of supreme indifference to her, and ought to be likewise to Doughy.

" I am here," she informed him, coldly.

While they had been conversing the sirens began wailing outside, and now an occasional bomb exploded in the vicinity of the Strada Stretta. The proprietor of the Balmoral considered it time to clear the café of customers, and take refuge in an air-raid shelter. Doughy found himself alone outside in the dark street.

At first he was quite satisfied with events. He had tried to find the girl. She wasn't to be found. That wasn't his fault. He had done what he set out to do. There hadn't been any hesitation on his part. It was just Fate. And that was that. . . .

This mood, however, did not last long. Doughy suddenly had a clear view of himself standing as the centre of all that desolating loneliness Sharman's death had created for him. He remembered his wretchedness during all these recent weeks and was filled with dread at the prospect of its continuing indefinitely. That girl offered him a chance of escape. He bloody well had to find her. . . .

Another bomb fell ; near enough for him to catch the fag-end of the blast. It blew into his memory a similar incident on an evening in Valetta not long ago when he was not alone. He seemed to hear the frightened voice of the Maltese girl : " I must go home to the shelter quick. I do not like it."

Well, here was another packet she wouldn't like. Wherever she was, ten to one she'd have fled " home to the shelter quick." That's where he'd find her. At any rate it was worth trying.

With the guns of the island still thudding, and bombs falling spasmodically, Doughy hurried along the Strada Reale and at the top turned into the Strada Mezzodi. In a minute or two he was outside the air-raid shelter to which he had conducted the girl on the night of their first acquaintance. He slipped round the blast wall at the entrance and dived down a series of dimly-lit steps for a distance of about forty feet. As he descended a queer noise, a mixture of murmuring voices in hundreds of different keys, rose to meet him.

At the foot of the steps he halted, taken aback a bit by

the sight confronting him. It was the first time he had been
in a Valetta air-raid shelter. Before him extended a long
wide tunnel hewn out of the limestone rock, and lit by
paraffin lamps suspended from the vaulted roof. Along
each side of the tunnel, for as far as he could see, stretched
iron bedsteads and wooden forms, jammed close together,
sometimes in pairs, leaving a narrow gangway along the
centre of the tunnel. Hundreds of Maltese of the poorer
class—men, women and children—filled the tunnel, sitting
or lying on the beds, smoking, and talking in groups. The
numbers reminded Doughy of the crowds in a street in
Senglea on a *festa* day, save that in this case the festival
spirit was anything but uppermost. He hadn't expected a
mob like this. It would make it pretty hard to spot the
girl, even if she were here.

He began to edge his way slowly along the centre gangway,
keeping a sharp eye to right and left of him. The light was
poor and was not much improved by the flickering of scores
of candles, burning before scores of pictures of the Virgin.
Doughy was the only English person to be seen. A Maltese
air-raid warden, with a red and white band on his arm,
gave him a nod as he passed, and a couple of Maltese V.A.D.'s
in grey-blue dresses and white caps with the Red Cross
stared at him interestedly. Two priests in little round
black hats, and half a dozen nuns moved quietly between
the rows of bedsteads, sustaining the more nervous of their
flock with a word of comfort. Every few yards a candle
burned in front of a picture of the Virgin under which flowers
were strewn, freesias and purple bougainvilleas. Before
these simple altars knelt little groups of the devout, mainly
women and children, telling their rosaries in a sing-song
murmur that never ceased. It was the combined effect of
all this fervid devotion that had struck so queerly on Doughy's
ears as he descended the steps to the shelter. Now, within
the confined tunnel it sounded to him more strange than
ever. An undercurrent of emotion, flowing on and on
beneath the more mundane scraps of chatter and conversation.
Subdued, yet the most unescapable thing in the shelter.
Impressive and, to Doughy's way of thinking, a bit uncanny.
On the occasions when a bomb fell close enough for the
explosion to sound loud within the shelter, the sing-song
murmur increased to a higher pitch of intensity, falling back

52

again, when the echoes had died away, to its normal low pitch and rhythm.

Doughy threaded his way through the crowded tunnel for fifty yards without any sign of the girl. The atmosphere became so hot and close that he removed his helmet. Not all the women knelt before the Virgin. Some were busy warming up dishes of macaroni over Primus stoves. Family groups squatted round little tables and forms eating and drinking. Many of them had been bombed out of their homes in the early raids of the war and had never gone back. Others were too terrified to remain above ground. The tunnel shelter was now their only home. Rarely did they venture outside. Here they dwelt like a new race of cave-dwellers, cooking, washing, sleeping, falling ill, love-making, quarrelling, all with an astonishing lack of privacy. The barefooted children played their games up and down the narrow gangway. Their fathers returned here to sleep after the day's work at the Dockyard was done.

Here and there, niches had been hollowed out of the tunnel walls, just big enough to hold a chair or two, a small table, or a small bed. Sometimes a curtain hung before the entrance enabling the inmates to obtain some semblance of privacy if they wished to retire from the communal life outside for a while. The tenants of these niches represented the more wealthy of the refugees. One had to pay £30 for the privilege of partly living in a niche in the wall. A whole tribe of relations, mothers, fathers, aunts, uncles, sons and daughters-in-law—for among the Maltese the family tie is a very powerful one—would club together to become the purchasers of a niche. But these were only the few. The vast bulk of the tunnel population had no other living space than the little area in front or the beds arranged alongside the walls, into which at night they fitted themselves as best they could.

Inside the shelter the air was thick, suffocating, fetid. There was no ventilation beyond that provided by the entrance to the tunnel. The stale, rancid smell of hundreds of crowded human bodies, mingling with other odours of which the reek of garlic was not the least penetrating, hit the newcomer from the open air with the force of a blow. At least, that is how it felt to Doughy. And the further he progressed into the shelter the worse it became.

" I'll be lucky if I get out of here alive," he said to himself.

Half-way along the tunnel he halted. There she was. He had found her. He stood in the gangway a few yards away from her while making sure that he wasn't mistaken. The girl had not noticed him. Barefooted, and with a white apron over her black frock, she was in the act of removing a loaf of bread from a big, round, straw provision basket which she had dragged from underneath a bed. Doughy decided that she wasn't pretty, but was as good as José's bride. Sitting on the edge of the bed was an old, fat, wrinkled Maltese woman with a *faldetta* on her head. Probably the mother, thought Doughy. Afterwards he was to learn that the girl like himself, was an orphan, and that the old woman was her aunt. Another old woman dressed entirely in black sat on a wooden form alongside the bed between two sharp-looking younger women who reminded Doughy in certain ways of the girl he had come in search of. They were, in fact, her married elder sisters, and their five young progeny were scrambling about their feet on the dusty floor of the shelter.

The girl raised her head from bending over the basket. Her eyes alighted on Doughy. She recognised him at once. She arranged her hair with a couple of swift pats and smiled. Doughy strode forward. He knew exactly how he would break the ice. He had recited the words to himself for the last half-hour.

" Thought I'd look you up as I was passing . . ." he began.

The rest of his carefully prepared introduction was drowned in an unexpected torrent. The four other women gave Doughy a shrewd look and then, all talking at once at the top of their voices, turned upon the girl, pouring out Maltese at a terrific rate.. Even the children joined in. The girl, on her part, was in no whit behindhand in reply.

" I don't know what it's all about, but she's giving as good as she's getting," thought Doughy.

Suddenly the chatter subsided as unexpectedly as it had begun. Doughy saw smiling friendly faces in front of him. The old woman on the bed made room for him to sit beside her. Instinctively he felt he had become a guest of honour.

" They ask what," said the girl in explanation of the excitement. " I tell them it was you save me."

Doughy opened his mouth to disclaim any such claim to distinction. But the words didn't shape themselves readily, and finding four pairs of feminine eyes studying him with embarrassing interest he remained dumb.

The party resumed its interrupted meal. The girl cut one of the Maltese loaves in half, tore out the centre, and crammed the hole with anchovies in oil. She offered it to Doughy. He refused politely on the strength of his recent fish-and-chips meal, which he post-dated by an hour or two. He lit a cigarette instead.

Among themselves the Maltese women kept up a continuous rattle of conversation, some of which the girl translated for Doughy's benefit and some not. He thought they seemed to be watching him very closely all the time. But in quite a friendly way. And on the few occasions when he ventured to make a remark to the girl, her relations were very quick in wanting to know what it was he had said. Nothing, so far as concerned him, escaped them.

This was all very well, but it wasn't what Doughy had come for. What with the heat of the shelter and the strain of sitting there under the piercing scrutiny of the four women, unable to understand a word they said, his discomfort increased minute by minute. He began to sweat so profusely that he had to loosen the neck of his battle-dress. He wondered whether he hadn't done enough for one night.

The old woman sitting beside him on the bed suddenly hoisted herself to her feet. She addressed a remark to the girl. A little argument seemed to arise, in which the other woman joined. When it was over the girl explained to Doughy:

" She say she make for you a tea."

A cup of tea was just what Doughy could do with at the moment. He accepted with thanks. The translation of this was greeted by all the other women with signs of approval, especially by the aged aunt who had made the suggestion. She boiled enough water on the Primus to make one cup of tea which she presented to Doughy. While he sipped it, she sat by his side, rapping out observations to the others which he could not understand, but which raised a laugh every now and then from the girl's married sisters. The loudest laugh of all came when the old woman unfastened a leather purse that hung from her neck by a chain. The purse hoarded

a few cheap trinkets and her identity disc. She extracted a
small, plain, well-worn silver ring and saying something in
Maltese, pretended to put it on her finger. The other women
went into fits of laughter. Doughy laughed too. The contrast
between the tiny ring and the thick podgy finger was funny
enough, whatever she was saying.

The cup of tea refreshed him. When he had finished he
felt more like going on with his business. By now the air-raid
had ended and the rosaries were being given a rest. Doughy
considered it time to extricate himself from the family party
and get down to serious business. He turned towards the
girl.

" What about me and you going to the pictures ? " he
said.

Smiles and unmistakable nods of approval from the relations
followed the girl's translation of the invitation. She took off
her apron and began putting on a pair of shoes.

All the relations, including the children, accompanied the
pair as they made their way out of the shelter, past the
curious eyes of the rows of refugees. Doughy grew alarmed.
Had something gone wrong with the invitation ? Was it
expected he was going to treat the whole bunch ? But
much to his relief they didn't follow any further than the
exit.

When alone at last with the girl in the street Doughy
asked :

" What's your name ? "

" Carmela," she replied. " Carmela Camilleri."

" Mine's easier. Harry," he said. " Think you can say it ? "

" Erry," was her attempt. " I talk the English good," she
laughed.


## VI—Gun Operations Room

As the Colonel entered R.H.Q. office the Adjutant glanced
at the memo. on the desk headed : " To O.C. 777th H.A.A.
Regt. from Brigade Major, Headquarters R.A."

" Just a reminder, sir, that you are on duty this evening
at G.O.R.," he said.

" Thanks," replied the Colonel. " For the moment it had

slipped my mind. I must warn my servant to get my bedding ready. I hope the mattress they give me won't be as damp as the one last time. It's quite bad enough having to put up with the icy cold. I've a good mind, too, to take my own chair. I can never find a seat in that place. They seem to think at G.O.R. that deputising for the A.A.D.C. necessitates standing on your feet for the best part of twenty-four hours. But I'll give' em another chance. Someone may offer me a chair this time. Who knows ? "

The Adjutant laughed. " Perhaps Peter will share his," he said. " He's duty officer with you."

" He'll be more willing to share his gossip," replied the Colonel. " If we happen to have a dull spell I shall return to-morrow laden with all the latest scandal of the island."

" I hope you do, sir," said the Adjutant. " Gossip has been getting terribly scarce recently. We're beginning to repeat ourselves in the Mess. . . . Our site will be well represented at G.O.R. to-day. We are also mounting guard there."

Peter was the Battery Commander of the regiment's other gun-site on the opposite side of Valetta. In addition to his outstanding abilities as a Gunner, he possessed a perfect genius for getting early news of what was going on, behind the scenes at G.H.Q. and elsewhere. As a source of secret and prior information on all sorts of subjects he was invaluable to the regiment. Time had proved, again and again, that Peter's information, however sensational, was usually correct.

The Colonel departed to instruct his servant to be sure and roll up a couple of extra blankets with his bedding.

Once every ten days or so it fell to the lot of each ack-ack Colonel on the island to take a turn as deputy for the A.A. Defence Commander at Gun Operations Room, the heart of Malta's defence. It was a twenty-four hour spell, and carried with it certain big responsibilities. Whoever was on duty, filled, for the time being, a position equivalent to commander-in-chief of all the gun-sites. He became direct adviser on all anti-aircraft matters to the Air Officer Commanding, upon whose shoulders lay the burden of responsibility for the defence of the island by air. The latter might want at any moment to put into being some plan needing very skilful co-operation on the part of the ground defences. Among other things the deputising A.A. colonel had to be ready to supply all the data required. " What is the maximum ceiling of your guns ? " . . . " How much fire-power can be brought to bear over such-and-such a part of the island ? " And so on.

At a few minutes before six in the evening the Colonel drove up to G.O.R. The officer he was relieving had already packed up and was waiting to quit.

"Thanks for being so punctual," he said. "I promised to meet my wife at the Snake Pit at six, and shall just do it."

The Snake Pit was the friendly name bestowed on the Ladies' Room at the Union Club in Valetta where married officers could entertain their wives, and flirtatious subalterns their girl friends.

"What's the state of the mattress ? " asked the Colonel.

"Humid," replied the other, and drove off.

A short tunnel led the Colonel to Gun Operations Room, situated well under ground level in a lofty and enormous " cavalier," one of those vault-like chambers hewn into the limestone foundations of the island by the old Knights of Malta in days gone by. Coming suddenly into this huge subterranean cavern from the warm daylight outside the Colonel felt as if he had stepped into a different world. There were no windows and the place was illuminated by electric bulbs hanging from the great domed roof. The air was still and cold, and possessed that damp, searching chill peculiar to cathedral crypts. The rough limestone walls were streaked with green stains like the sides of a cave in chalk cliffs by the sea. With the mouldy, earthy smell was mingled a decided tang from the oil-stoves that were supposed to provide the heating for the place. Although about a score of men were busy in the great vault everything seemed silent and stealthy. When they spoke to one another their voices sounded a trifle hollow and unnatural, half-lost in the muffled echoes from the domed roof above. The slightest disturbance, even the scraping of a chair on the floor, produced its echo.

One end of this long, chilly chamber was divided by canvas screens, eight feet high, into a series of cubicles. most of them used by the R.A.F. for pay offices, cipher offices, and the accommodation of clerks. Of these cubicles one was allotted as sleeping quarters to the officer deputising for the A.A. Defence Commander. The Colonel entered. The cubicle contained nothing except an issue iron bedstead and a mattress. He carefully ran his hand over the latter and

58

was relieved to find it was not so moist as he had expected.

"Make my bed up so that I'm lying on four doubled blankets," he ordered his servant. "It's from underneath that the cold strikes most."

The remainder of the vault, about forty feet of it, was the province of Gun Operations Room proper. Partitioned off in one corner, was the office of the A.O.C. Along the wall at the far end, the Gunner duty-officer sat before a desk on a raised bench, rather like a schoolmaster. At his elbow was a telephonist with an exchange connected to all the gun sites on the island and to Headquarters R.A. Close by, at a desk sat the searchlight duty-officer, also with his own telephonist and exchange. Other telephones kept G.O.R. in direct touch with the Governor, the Vice-Admiral, and Civil Defence authorities. An immense table covered by an outline map of Malta, the neighbouring island of Gozo, and the southern half of Sicily, occupied the entire centre of the room. Conspicuous on this map was marked the position of the island's Radio Directional Finding station. From this point radiated bearing lines drawn across the map at every ten degrees. The same point was also the centre of a number of concentric circles—at intervals of a five-mile radius, so that the whole conveyed the impression of a succession of spoked wheels of increasing circumference. Around the table were seated a number of R.A.F. " tellers,' each armed with a rake resembling that of a croupier. The other occupant of the table was an R.A.F. sergeant, with earphones clamped on. He was in direct telephonic communication with the R.D.F. station.

On entering Gun Operations Room the Colonel took a swift glance at the table. No signs of activity were manifest among the " tellers " so he knew there wasn't a raid on. He walked across the room, hearing faint echoes of his footsteps all the time, to have a word with the R.A.F. Group Captain, who was the right-hand man of the Air Officer Commanding. The Navy representative at G.O.R., a Lieutenant-Commander, had a table next to him. It was the latter's business to provide all information that might be required concerning shipping movements.

"What about that convoy?" the Colonel inquired of the latter.

"What convoy?" blandly replied the Lieut.-Commander.

" The one that's been going to arrive ever since Mussolini came in," said the Colonel banteringly. " That's nearly three months ago and we haven't seen it yet. You know what the natives are saying ? "

" What ? "

" They are all beginning to wonder whether Mare Nostrum isn't an Italian lake after all."

" Perhaps if they wait a little longer they'll find out."

" Ah, so you do know something ? "

The Lieut.-Commander clamped down. " Nothing for publication," he said. " Only a guess on my part."

The Colonel laughed. " Hear that ? " he said, turning to the Group Captain. " The Silent Service doing its stuff. . . ."

" By the way," interposed the Group Captain, " the A.O.C. is a bit peeved. He's had one or two more complaints from pilots about being fired on by your gunners."

" Complaints be damned," retorted the Colonel indignantly. " If it comes to that I can lodge a few complaints myself. Your fellows have had orders from the A.O.C. himself that when returning from reconnaissance they are to fly in at a certain height so as not to be fired at. Do they stick to the rules ? Not on your life. They come in at whatever height they think they will. What do you suggest the gunners are to do ? Take a chance and not fire ? We'd get the blame if we happened to let an enemy plane through. The trouble usually occurs when the recces are coming in from a sortie, either at early dawn or late in the evening. Just the times when it's very difficult to distinguish whether it's an enemy or not."

" I'll inform the A.O.C. of what you say," said the Group Captain.

" Yes, do," replied the Colonel.

He strolled across the room to where Peter, the Gunner duty-officer, was perched before his raised desk. They exchanged a few words about domestic matters concerning Peter's battery and then the Colonel asked :

" What news have you got ? I promised not to return to the Fort empty-handed."

" Not much, I'm afraid," replied the Battery Commander, after a moment's reflection. " I suppose you know there's a convoy coming in to-morrow night ? "

" I didn't know. That's very, very interesting," said the Colonel, giving a quick glance across the room in the direction of the Lieut.-Commander. " Are you quite certain, Peter ? "

" Positive, sir. On the best authority. Of course, I can't . . ."

" No, you can't mention names. No names, no pack-drill," laughed the Colonel. " Was it by any chance the Lieutenant-Commander over there ? "

" Indeed, no. From much higher up."

" You're a wonder, Peter," said the Colonel. " You don't mind if I tell the Lieutenant-Commander ? He doesn't know."

Pleased with the idea, he was about to cross the room when a stir of life became evident at the big table in the centre of the vault. The R.A.F. sergeant was listening attentively to his earphones and writing down a message coming over from the Radio Directional Finding Station.

" Something's breaking," said Peter.

A sense of big expectancy seemed to have immediately gripped everyone. In an instant the whole atmosphere of the place changed with the stirring of an undercurrent of activity. It was as though a stronger pulse had suddenly started to beat.

The Colonel joined the Group Captain before the centre table.

" Air Observe . . . Air Observe . . ." came the low, clear voice of the telephonist beside the Gunnery duty-officer as he despatched the preliminary warning to all gun-sites.

At the big table the R.A.F. sergeant was passing on to a " teller " the information about the air-raid that was developing.

" It was a " 4 plus " raid—four or more machines—coming in from a bearing of 15 degrees at a height of 12,000 feet.

" Fifty miles . . ."

The " teller " marked the position of the enemy planes on the map.

The Group Captain took a few quick steps over to the wall where hung the board on which was recorded R.A.F. information—the exact number of fighter planes available to go up on the instant from each of the aerodromes, the number of machines being overhauled at that particular moment, the number of reconnaissance planes out and the times they were due back, the number of bombers out, if any. After a rapid glance at the situation the Group Captain got through by telephone direct to an aerodrome.

" Four bandits approaching . . . Bearing, One-Five degrees . . . Tiger Flight . . . Scramble. . . ."

Immediately another " teller " at the table added the information to the map that fighters were in action.

On the wall near the R.A.F. board was a press-button with a red electric bulb glowing beside it. This was the main siren button for the island and the red light indicated that all was well with the working of the circuit.

The Group Captain pressed the button and, though no sound penetrated into the deep-sunk vault, the occupants knew that all over the island the sirens were vociferously uttering their warning to the population.

" Alert . . . Alert . . ."

The gunner telephonist was busy sending out the information about the raiders to the gun sites in the form of an A.K. message written out for him by the duty-officer from the ' plot ' on the centre table where not a movement escaped his eye.

Now the pilots of Tiger flight were wirelessing back their movements direct to Gun Operations Room, and receiving in return any information that would help them to find the enemy. As their position in the air changed so the " teller " altered the position on the map.

Twenty-five miles . . .

Not for the first time the Colonel, watching all the moves on the table, found himself fascinated by this silent drama that was being played out under his eyes like some child's game. It was difficult in that calm, unbustled atmosphere, away from all the stir, noise and agitation of the outside world, to realise the life and death issues that hung on these alterations on the map. A faint air of unreality tinged it all. He imagined the scene on the gun-site at Fort Pedro that very moment. The gunners at their stations. The predictor and height-finder crews getting on to the target. The Gun Position Officer's megaphone bawling orders. The gun-layers glued to their dials. The clang of the breeches as they swung-to behind the shells. How real that all seemed by comparison . . . Yet he was forced to admit that by sheer contrast, by just this same touch of unreality, the drama as unfolded in the chill depths of Gun Operations Room had a peculiar gripping power such as he never experienced at the Fort during a raid.

" Bearing, Two-O degrees. . . . One-O miles. . . ."

" At this rate," thought the Colonel, " it won't be long before they clash."

From his exchange at the side of the room the gunner telephonist continued sending all fresh information to the gun-sites.

Five miles . . .

" We ought to be hearing from the guns," murmured the Group Captain to the Colonel, after a moment or two.

As if in direct reply came the voice of the gunner telephonist announcing the first site to report being in action.

" Pedro shot . . ."

The Colonel experienced a mild satisfaction that his guns had opened the ball though he knew that it was purely fortuitous and depended on the direction the raiders were coming in from. The duty-officer despatched a gunner to a board on the wall bearing the names of all the gun-sites on the island. Against each name was a hook. On the Fort Pedro hook the gunner hung a red disc, the sign that it had come into action. In the next few seconds arrived a rush of reports from other gun-sites, and soon the board was dabbed all over with red discs.

The pace of time seemed to have quickened. Mere seconds now seemed to be charged with import. It was difficult to believe that only a few minutes had passed since the first warning reached Gun Operations Room.

" Pedro-site calling . . ." suddenly announced the gunner at the telephone exchange. " Enemy plane shot down . . . Bearing, Two-Five degrees . . . One-Eight-Four-One hours (6.41 p.m.) . . ."

Almost immediately came a report of an enemy plane shot down from another site giving a different bearing.

" Confirmation. Same plane," remarked the Group Captain laconically, after a quick mental calculation from the bearing lines on the map.

" Sounds like one for the Gunners," observed the Colonel, at the same time thinking how much the attitude of the little group watching the proceedings, himself included, resembled

63

that of the hardened gambler at a roulette table upon whose impassive exterior even a fortunate turn of the wheel fails to make any mark.

The Lieutenant-Commander was telephoning details of the position of the crashed plane down to the Harbour so that a rescue launch could be despatched to pick up any survivors.

Suddenly, to the Group-Captain's intense satisfaction the wireless operator in touch with the fighter planes received the message he had been eagerly awaiting.

" Tiger leader calling . . . Tiger leader calling . . . Tiger flight engaging . . . Tally-Ho . . ."

" It won't be long before it's over now," commented the Group Captain.

As indicated on the map the planes, British and enemy alike, were over the Harbour area. Bombs were falling, guns were roaring, buildings crashing. But scarcely an echo of the inferno outside reached the ears of the little group in Gun Operations Room whose labours had once more attained the moment of fruition. Once again the Colonel, picturing in his mind's eye the drama being enacted outside their walls, a drama in which they themselves, though unseen, played principal parts, was struck by the violence of the contrast. The unreality within culminating in the tremendous realism outside. . . . Just as if, at the end of some puppet tragedy, the marionettes were to start bleeding real blood instead of sawdust.

Soon the enemy planes were signalled in retreat. Twenty miles . . . thirty miles . . . Here a Hurricane wirelessed back that it had shot down another enemy plane.

" Not so bad. Two out of four," commented the Group Captain. " I hope they get the lot."

Forty miles . . . Fifty miles . . . Sixty miles . . .

" That's over," said the Group Captain. He walked across the room and pressed the button to sound the " All Clear " on the sirens throughout the island. The gunner telephonist sent the " Raiders Passed " signal to all the gun-sites.

Within Gun Operations Room the heightened pulse of the past twenty minutes began to re-assume its normal beat. From the gun-sites dribbled in the routine reports of number of rounds fired, casualties to personnel (if any), casualties to equipment, planes seen and at what height. The Colonel withdrew his eyes from the great map on the table with a grunt of satisfaction, just as one relaxes when the curtain descends on a good theatrical performance. He remembered he had been about to do something when the raid broke in. The sight of the Lieutenant-Commander talking to the Air Intelligence Officer reminded him. He sauntered across to his table. The Air Intelligence Officer was saying :

" Would you be good enough to let me know the instant the rescue launch returns. If there are any survivors I want to interrogate them without delay."

The Lieutenant-Commander promised to do so. He turned towards the Colonel.

" I've some important news for you," said the Colonel, with a twinkle in his eye. " Something you don't know. A convoy's arriving to-morrow night. Positive."

The Lieutenant-Commander grinned back at him.

" Funny I shouldn't have known," he said.

Satisfied at having made his little score the Colonel walked off to discover what there was to eat in the canteen.

Meanwhile, outside Gun Operations Room, Smiler leaned against the open doorway of the guard-room having a last cigarette before going on guard. Suddenly he opened his eyes wider. A couple of people were walking along the road towards him. One he knew and one he didn't.

" So that's it ! " he exclaimed grinning, when Doughy, solemn-faced as ever, with Carmela hanging on his arm, approached within range. " I heard you'd been and decorated yourself with a Maltese Cross. How long you known her ? "

Doughy, looking none too pleased at the unexpected encounter, remained silent. Smiler turned his attention to the girl, running her over with a quick, appraising glance.

" Well, well, well," he said. " And aren't you a big girl for fourteen."

" She's eighteen," muttered Doughy.

" Dear  me . . . How  time  flies," Smiler  remarked, banteringly. " And what did they baptise you ? "

" Her  name's Carmela.  Carmela  Camilleri," Doughy grunted.

" Blimey.  What  opera  does  she  sing  in ? " grinned Smiler. " No, don't go away yet, Doughy. I've got another minute."

Like a connoisseur in such matters he passed the girl

under examination again from top to toe. Carmela smiled back at him in a friendly manner.

"How do you like the war?" he inquired.

She shook her head vigourously. "I not like it."

"Can't blame you," said Smiler.

"Erry not like it also," she added.

"Erry? Who's Erry?"

She indicated the silent, solemn Doughy.

"Oh, you mean him. We always call him Doughy. Just as I'm always called Smiler."

"Smee-ler," she practised, prettily.

"That's good . . . Of course, I've got another name. Like Doughy has . . . Want to know it?"

"She doesn't," interrupted Doughy, goaded into words by a jealous fear of losing his treasure.

"Why?"

"She's not interested."

"Let her speak for herself. She's got a tongue, hasn't she?" replied Smiler. He addressed Carmela again: "You want to know, don't you?"

"I-want-to-know-all," she said simply, picking out the words slowly and with difficulty.

"Quite right, Carmela," exclaimed Smiler, with a grin. "As a young girl should. And I'm the right sort of bloke to teach you. Anything you want to know, ask me. What's first?"

"Start by telling her about your wife in England," said the glowering Doughy in a sudden flash of inspiration.

Smiler turned on him a long, more-in-sorrow-than-in-anger look. Next moment his customary grin re-asserted itself.

"So poor Erry doesn't like the war, either," he said with a pretence of deep concern. "Now, isn't that too bad. Better not let the Colonel know. He would be pained."

"You like the war, Smee-ler?" inquired the girl.

"Well, you see, Carmela, with us it isn't a matter of like or dislike. We've got to do it."

"I got to do it, too."

"That's the stuff," said Smiler.

"My aunt . . . my uncle . . . They got to do it, too,' she continued with pride.

"Better an' better. Where are they doing it?"

" In the air-raid shelter."

Smiler greeted this statement with the straightest of faces.

" I guess there are more ways than one of winning the war," he said.

Out of the guard-room suddenly bustled a sergeant. His appearance, much to Doughy's satisfaction, terminated the conversation.

" Reliefs ! . . . Fall in ! . . ."

" See you again, Carmela," shouted Smiler, grabbing his rifle.


## VII—Enter the Luftwaffe

" Isn't to-night Peter's gala night ? " the Colonel mentioned one morning in R.H.Q. office.

" Yes, sir," replied the Adjutant.

" That means another bottle of the Bristol Cream. Any left ? I shouldn't like him to be disappointed."

The Adjutant laughed, well-knowing Peter's weakness.

" I'll ask the Mess Secretary," he said. " If there is, Peter must have it."

Peter, as already stated, was Battery Commander of the regiment's other battery stationed on the Three Cities side of the Harbour. It was the custom for him to dine, more or less ceremonially, once a month at R.H.Q. Mess at Fort Pedro. On these occasions he was by way of being an honoured guest and the Colonel liked to do him proud. Peter, an indefatigable news-gatherer, always brought with him all the latest gossip of G.H.Q. Which made him doubly welcome.

" I'm looking forward to a lot of new juicy scandal, sir," continued the Adjutant. " All the real dirt."

" Wonderful how Peter finds the stuff," the Colonel said. " I visit G.H.Q. far more frequently than he does and never hear half as much. Peter and a secret have an irresistible attraction for one another."

" He must have a jungle telephone attached to every brass-hat," concluded the Adjutant.

By now Christmas had come and gone. It was the second

day of the New Year. During the intervening weeks Fort
Pedro, and Valetta, too, for that matter, had become so
accustomed to Italian air-raids that only the few odd days
when nothing happened seemed worth remembering. In
the Command Post the telephonist now headed his A.K.
messages from Gun Operations Room with a serial number
already running into three figures. To say nothing of the
hundred and more occasions the guns had been manned on
the receipt of an " Air Observe " which had not developed
into a raid.

In the six months that had passed since the shock, the
Maltese population had regained a satisfactory degree of confidence in the power of the island defences to protect them.
The run on the banks had stopped, business was resumed,
traffic was almost normal, shops and cafés were opened. The
official order making it compulsory for everyone to take shelter
during an air-raid was no longer enforced. Crowds now
gathered in the streets of Valetta and cheered as they watched
the shells of the barrage burst round the enemy planes.
They developed a great contempt for the Italian airmen
who never dared fly lower than about 15,000 feet. In this
they were not entirely justified, for this high-level bombing
never became indiscriminate, and few bombs fell outside the
target areas. But for this the damage to residential property
and the number of civilian casualties would have been much
greater in the first six months than they were. Not that
they were negligible, as it was. But the Maltese faced their
sufferings bravely. They were cheered daily by the spectacle
of the gunners shooting enemy planes out of the sky. And
after the first few weeks their confidence received a tonic—
the arrival on the island of some Hurricane fighters. Henceforth " Faith," " Hope," and " Charity " the three gallant
Gloucester-Gladiators, no longer had to bear the entire
brunt of the fighting in the air.

It was just after six in the evening when Peter, stout,
red-faced and jolly-looking, drove in his car through the
entrance to Fort Pedro. The Colonel, the Adjutant, and the
other diners were already assembled in the ante-room of
the Mess. They included the Battery Commander of the
Fort Pedro gun-site, and the Battery Captain. The latter
was also Tactical Control Officer, a new job called into being
by the frequency of the air-raids. His task was to plot the

raids in the Command Post, thus leaving the Gun Position Officer free to give his unhampered attention to the business of fighting the guns. The T.C.O. would be called by runner if wanted, but was in hopes of being allowed, for once, an undisturbed meal. There was also in the party an Army padre, and a subaltern with his guest, 'a Flight-Lieutenant from a squadron of Mark I Hurricanes. He had fought in the Battle of Britain and had but recently arrived on the island.

Peter entered the ante-room closely followed, in accordance with the Adjutant's private instructions, by a Maltese steward carrying a tray upon which stood a sherry glass and a complete bottle of Bristol Cream. He settled down immediately to show how he much appreciated this swift attention.

" I understood you had Navy stewards, sir," remarked the Flight-Lieutenant, eyeing the back of the departing Maltese.

" Not since the Sub-Mariners left us," explained the Colonel. " They went some time ago. And very sorry we were . . . Grand fellows. But after Mussolini came in they grew so numerous they had to go to bigger quarters. Extraordinary how we gradually fell into their ways. If they'd remained much longer we'd have turned into something resembling Marines. I'll give you an instance. The Brigadier told me that one day, when I had gone to Valetta, he asked for me at the entrance to the Fort and was informed by the sentry that I had ' gone ashore '."

The padre chimed in, turning to the Flight-Lieutenant : " When we shared the Mess with the Sub-Mariners we used to have Divine Service down at the gymnasium on the jetty. A Naval Chaplain officiated. One Sunday the Army Chaplain-General decided he ought to come and look us up, and preach a sermon. He opened with these remarks which, I consider, show he possesses a nice sense of humour. ' I had heard it rumoured that the gunners at Fort Pedro were becoming distinctly nautical. But I think it took the ship's biscuit just now when I heard your Chaplain announce : *We will now sing Hymn Number* 257. *It will be found amidships in the book* ' ".

In the laugh that followed the Adjutant ostentatiously replenished Peter's glass.

" Now earn it," he said.

The red-faced Battery Commander flattened a big sip of
Bristol Cream against his palate, looked meditatively at his
glass and said :

" The Luftwaffe are in Sicily."

In the room the chatter died away. Everyone stopped
drinking and stared at the Battery Commander in silence.
Satisfied with the effect of his announcement he slowly
emptied his glass.

" Are you sure ? " demanded the Colonel, after a moment.
" I know there have been vague rumours. But it has always
been denied. The G.O.C. was here looking over the Fort
yesterday. He didn't hint a word."

He addressed the Flight-Lieutenant : " Your people ought
to know something about this, if it is true."

" It's a complete surprise to me, sir," was the reply. " I
can hardly believe our Wing-Co. knows anything. He would
have been certain to mention it. Of course, the Air Officer
Commanding may know. If so, he's keeping it pretty close."

" I gather that the rumour has taken strong hold on the
poorer sections of the Maltese," said the padre. " This
morning my friend Father Ambrose stopped me in the
Strada Reale and mentioned it. He wanted to know if
I could tell him anything to allay the anxiety in his
parish."

" You can't, padre," the Battery Commander said, briefly.
" The Luftwaffe are in Sicily, and that's all there is to it.
I was told an hour ago on the best authority."

" Who ? " asked the Colonel.

" Somebody on the G.O.C.'s staff. I can't mention names,
sir."

" Dinner is served," announced the white-jacketed Maltese
steward from the doorway.

During the meal the coming of the Luftwaffe provided the
one topic of conversation. The Battery Commander's information exerted both a sobering and exciting effect. Knowing
what had happened in London, Coventry, Plymouth and other
cities at home they all realised full well that they would be
in for something compared with which the past six months
spelt picnic. At the same time the prospect of a test with
the Germans, real adversaries, pleased and stimulated them.
The Flight-Lieutenant, on the strength of his experience
in the Battle of Britain was plied with questions, and com-

parisons were drawn between Italian and German bombing tactics with much reference to dive-bombing.

" The Ju. 87's—the dive-bombers—won't worry us a bit, sir," he cheerfully assured the Colonel. " Our Hurricanes will knock 'em off the ceiling like flies. I'm not so sure about the Ju. 88's. I rather fancy they have the legs on us for speed now. And should they produce any of their latest Me. 109's . . . well, we could do with a few Spitfires."

In the middle of all the talk a waiter approached the Tactical Control Officer and whispered in his ear. The T.C.O. cursed at the prospect of another good dinner spoiled. He rose to go.

" Raid ? " queried the Colonel.

" Yes, sir. Air Observe."

" If its I-ti's we'll keep your food hot," the red-faced Battery Commander called after him as he disappeared. " If it's the Luftwaffe, we won't promise."

It proved to be neither. This time the raid did not mature, and the T.C.O. was back before the dinner ended.

Shortly afterwards the subaltern and his guest disappeared into the ante-room whence soon proceeded the sound of the wireless spouting Italian.

" Jimmie wouldn't be able to sleep at night if he didn't know what was going on in Rome," laughed the Adjutant.

Suddenly the wireless ceased. The subaltern appeared in the doorway of the Mess looking rather serious.

" Rome official has just announced that a German air contingent is about to participate in the air and naval struggle in the Mediterranean," he said.

" That settles it," said the Colonel in the silence with which this news was greeted. " We can expect the Luftwaffe any moment."

Nevertheless days passed without sign of the Luftwaffe. Not only that. Italian air activity greatly diminished too. Malta enjoyed its quietest spell for months. In Valetta the more sanguine of the inhabitants took this for a good sign. The pessimists regarded it as the ominous lull before the storm. Once more donkey-carts and hand-barrows appeared in the streets, wheeling little stacks of household belongings to the safety of tunnel shelters and outlying villages. The evacuation was on nothing like the previous scale. But there was no doubt of the new dreads the advent of the

71

Luftwaffe had implanted in the hearts of large sections of
the Maltese, despite their faith in the island defences.

Just over a week went by in this comparative calm. One
afternoon the Colonel, standing with the Battery Commander
on the verandah at Fort Pedro after lunch, suddenly spotted
three planes approaching the island from the north-west, the
direction of Sicily.

" Odd-looking Hurricanes," he remarked, raising his
binoculars for a closer examination. " They're not Hurricanes
at all," he added after a moment or two. " They're Fleet
Air Arm fighters. Fulmers . . . Where the devil have they
come from ? "

" Off some aircraft-carrier, I expect," said the Battery
Commander.

They watched the flight of Fulmers fly in from the sea over
Valetta and land on an aerodrome.

" First time I've seen Fulmers land on the island," commented the Colonel, curious. " I wonder what their
business is ? "

The answer was in the Command Post, at that identical
moment. The telephonist was scribbling down on his
message-pad, as fast as his pencil could move, a signal just
arriving from Gun Operations Room. He handed it over to
the Gun Position Officer. The signal read :

> " *G.O.R. to all gun-sites. Stand by . . . Aircraft-
> Carrier ILLUSTRIOUS damaged . . . Putting
> into Grand Harbour.*"

The G.P.O. jumped to the door of the shelter.

" Numbers One ! . . ." he roared through the megaphone.

The four sergeants from the gun-pits doubled-up. He read
them the message. In a few seconds the gun-crews were
ready for action. Then he sent a runner to the Colonel with
the news.

The Colonel hurried into the Command Post.

" Get through to the Gun Control Officer," he ordered the
telephonist. " Peter's on duty at G.O.R. to-day," he
explained to the G.P.O. " He may be able to tell us something more."

" Gun Control Officer, sir," said the telephonist, in a
moment or two.

The Colonel took the earphones. " That you, Peter ? "

he said. " The Colonel speaking . . . What's the dope on this *Illustrious* business ? "

" As far as we know from the V.A.M. (Vice-Admiral, Malta) " replied Peter, " she was out on a protective sweep in the Sicilian Channel and got it badly from the Luftwaffe . . . Dive-bombed . . . Yes, badly damaged. That's all we know. Except that she has just called for fighter protection and is making her way here with destroyer escort."

" That's likely to make things pretty hot here," commented the Colonel.

" It is, sir. By the way, I'm off duty at six o'clock and propose coming over to the Fort to discuss with you and the other Battery Commander what we are going to do about it."

The Colonel relinquished the 'phone.

" Dive-bombed badly by the Luftwaffe," he informed the G.P.O. " They are bound to follow her here. It's going to be a great fight."

As he left the Command Post there was a roar overhead. Looking up he saw the flight of Fulmers, followed by half a dozen Hurricanes, speeding seawards to the assistance of the battered giant.

Towards the end of the afternoon the Adjutant entered the office.

" The troops on the gun-site are pretty excited, sir," he said. " They've just spotted the *Illustrious* coming in."

" How far out is she ? " asked the Colonel.

" About two miles."

" I'll just finish this report to the C.R.A. and then come and have a look."

When the Colonel emerged on the ramparts of the Fort, though the day was drawing to a close, the *Illustrious* was close enough in for him to see, with the help of glasses, little figures moving about the flight deck. On the smooth waters the great, naked hull of the ship seemed to loom larger than ever, as if charged and magnified by the drama that surrounded her. She was labouring slowly under her own steam, a very weary Titan. Behind, before, and on each side of her raced four destroyers, like angry terriers, hurling tall cascades of white foam from their bows. Looking through his glasses the Colonel noticed that the aircraft-carrier

appeared to be considerably down by the stern, and that a
multiple pom-pom, forrard of the control tower, had received
a direct hit and disappeared.   He watched, not unstirred
by the significance of the occasion, till the vessel slipped out
of sight behind Fort St. Elmo into Grand Harbour.

Later on the Colonel had to pay a visit to the Dockyard
gun-site where a Bofors had been added to the original naval
pom-pom, the latter having been taken over by Dockyard
personnel.   The sergeant on the Bofors gun had just received
news that his wife had been killed in an air-raid in England,
and the Colonel wished to express his personal sympathy.
As he drove through Valetta he could feel the excitement
aroused among the residents by the arrival of the *Illustrious*.
Crowds of Maltese, men, women and children, thronged the
streets, and all seemed to be making for the direction
of the Dockyard.

The Colonel offered the Bofors sergeant his condolences.

" I won't feel better, sir, till I knock one of them Huns
down," said the sergeant.    " A Hun.  Not an I-ti.  An I-ti
won't satisfy me now."

" Well, you look like getting your chance soon," the
Colonel replied.

He strolled over to the edge of the bastion on which the
gun-site was situated.   It overlooked the creek where the
*Illustrious* now lay docked beside the quay, sixty sheer feet
below.   Crowds of Maltese lined the tops of all the bastions
overlooking the Harbour.   The quay had been swept clear
of all but those who had business there.   Drawn up alongside
were row upon row of Red Cross ambulances.   Stretchers,
one after another without a break, were being carried down
a gangway by sailor and soldier stretcher-bearers from an
opening in the interior of the vessel.   The wounded lay
tucked in blankets, most of them with grey faces and eyes
closed.   Some wore blood-stained bandages round their heads.
Nurses from the Military Hospital in their grey and red
uniform hovered around the open ambulances.   Over all the
deep silence of a solemn ceremonial prevailed, interrupted
only by the sound of ambulances driving off, and the shout
of an occasional order.

Down the gangway, after the stretchers, came the walking
wounded and the shell-shock cases.   The pitiful spectacle
presented by the latter was alone evidence of the *Illustrious's*

ordeal. Bombs had dropped down the lift-hatches and exploded inside the ship, causing a terrific concussion in the confined space. The shock cases showed all that. Fixed white faces, staring eyes, some of the men staggering as if drunk, others afraid to set one foot before another. One man's hands trembled so violently he couldn't light a cigarette. A soldier lit it for him and placed it between his lips. A few of the men were crying. One poor fellow's legs suddenly collapsed beneath him and he had to be lifted off by two sailors. Watching all this the Colonel half-dreaded to hear, at any moment, the sudden wail of the warning sirens.

These wrecks of fine strong men were loaded into lorries and driven away. Her dead, the *Illustrious* kept to herself, to be buried at sea later on.

As a relief from the depressing sight the Colonel turned to examine the damage sustained by the ship itself. And this, in its way, was equally depressing. Bomb fragments had pitted the super-structure with holes, like a colander. Two or three great gaping rents in the flight deck showed where the dive bombers had scored direct hits. On one of the lifts still working, the wreckage of planes was being hoisted up from below—Swordfish, Albacores, Fulmers—many a mere mass of twisted metal. A faint odour of charred wood rose with the wreckage and drifted upwards in the air. Already derricks were busy unloading the mess into lighters.

He took another look at the pom-pom near the control turret. Nothing was left but bits of scrap metal lying amid a heap of empty cartridge cases. At the same time he was astonished to notice that the pom-pom nearest to it appeared to be entirely undamaged. All along the sides of the flight deck stood groups of Navy gunners ready to swing the aircraft-carrier's 4.5 ack-ack guns into action in the event of a sudden attack.

The Colonel walked thoughtfully away from the bastion. His first sight of the havoc and precision of a dive-bombing attack had made a deep impression. He realised fully the grim times ahead for everyone on the island. On returning to Fort Pedro he found the two Battery Commanders awaiting the conference. He described all he had seen.

" It's certain we shall be called upon to defend the *Illustrious* from the dive-bombers," he concluded.

" That's what we wanted to talk to you about, sir," said

75

Peter. " It's quite clear that with ordinary height-control fire we can't stop these dive-bombers. John, here, and I have come to the conclusion that the only answer is some other sort of barrage, which we will work out between us so that the two sites won't overlap."

" I expect that something will come through from G.O.R. about it," the Colonel said. " But in the meantime go ahead. How do you propose to work it ? "

The two Battery Commanders expounded their ideas. In the barrage there would be a carpet of bursts through which the dive-bombers, to be accurate, would have to dive. It entailed careful judgment of the height. If this were too high the bombers could come in underneath the carpet. If too low, they could release their bombs accurately before reaching it. So a happy medium had to be struck.

The three of them discussed the matter thoroughly and decided to work out a barrage for the regiment's two gun-sites.

" I have only one thing more to add," said the Colonel. " It's under half an hour's flying time from Sicily."

" Yes, sir. Time presses," nodded the B.C. of the Pedro site. " Come up to my room, Peter. I've got a map. It's a race now between us and the Luftwaffe."

## VIII—ATTACK ON THE *ILLUSTRIOUS*

Two days passed. Two days of which every hour was packed tight with expectation. And to everyone's surprise the Luftwaffe still had not struck. Each day since the arrival of the *Illustrious* in Grand Harbour a German reconnaissance plane, christened by the Fort Pedro gunners " Gunboat Joe," flew over Grand Harbour. But that was all. The recce always flew in at a great height, between 20,000 and 25,000 feet ; and though it faced the concentrated fire of all the batteries, was never touched.

Early in the morning the Colonel, wading through the routine battery returns at R.H.Q. office, was interrupted by the arrival of a Don R. with a message from Gun Operations Room.

" A barrage is being worked out by the A.A.D.C. (Anti-Aircraft Deputy Commander) " it stated. " There will be a consultation at R.A. Headquarters between the A.A.D.C. and Regimental Commanders at 1130 hours (11.30 a.m.) when the plan and suggestions will be discussed.

The Colonel went in search of the Battery Commander and found him on the gun-site.

" I'm afraid all your hard work has been wasted," he said. " I've just been informed by G.O.R. that they're working out a barrage for us which, I presume, will include all the guns on the island, and any ships in harbour. Also the *Illustrious*. How far have you got ? "

" We finished last night, sir. Of course, with only two sites we couldn't cover a large area, it's only a thin barrage. I don't mind the waste of time. I'm only too glad to know H.Q. is really on the job."

" Yours might be useful," said the Colonel. " I'll take it along with me to the conference and tell them you and Peter worked it out, and they can have it if it's of service to them. In any case, it'll show 'em we haven't been asleep."

The conference at R.A. Headquarters in Valetta met in the old hall of an historic building, adorned with a beautifully decorated ceiling dating back to the middle of the eighteenth century. Suits of armour, the one-man tanks of battles long ago, gleamed in the corners of the apartment. A large-scale map of Malta covered a great space on one of the walls. Down the centre of the hall ran a long trestle table with folding chairs.

When the Colonel arrived he found the commanders of other A.A. regiments already present. Soon they were joined by the gunnery officer of the *Illustrious*, and one or two naval lieutenants from destroyers in the Harbour. A major from the Royal Malta Artillery came in followed by the Air Liaison Officer. Punctually at eleven-thirty the A.A. Deputy Commander himself showed up, and they all took their seats at the table.

" Gentlemen," began the A.A.D.C. " I don't want to waste any time. So my remarks will be brief. The reason we are here is to discuss the formation of a barrage to defend the *Illustrious* against any form of air attack. A barrage of this kind, to be of any success, must have perfect co-ordination between all gun-sites, whether ashore or afloat. My staff and myself are working on the details of the land gun-sites. I shall be very pleased if all ship commanders will let me know their number of guns, calibres, and where the ship is moored, so that these can be incorporated into what I shall term the 'standing part' of the barrage. Gentlemen, our object must be to lay a thick carpet of bursts over the *Illustrious* through which it will be certain destruction for any plane to attempt to dive. I need hardly say how urgent this task is. We may expect an attack at any moment. I am sure I can rely upon your whole-hearted co-operation."

A staff officer unfolded a big map of the Harbour area. Across the top of it in bold, black lettering, stood out the words : GRAND HARBOUR BARRAGE.

None of them failed to be impressed by the importance of the occasion. But none of them realised, seeing these words for the first time, that here was a moment which would pass into history. They were, indeed, officiating at the birth of one of the wonders of the War. Grand Harbour Barrage, destined in the months to come to spread fear into the hearts of their boldest enemy. Grand Harbour Barrage, destined to wring from the Luftwaffe the admission that it was " the fiercest thing we ever had to face." Grand Harbour Barrage, destined to play so great a part in the salvation of Malta. And, possibly, in the salvation of much else of the British Empire besides.

The conference crowded round the unfolded map. The work was not yet complete. Some of the areas had already been allotted to regiments. Others remained to be apportioned.

" What are the arrangements for Bofors ? " queried a Major who was representing a light A.A. regiment.

" The scheme does not include Bofors or pom-poms," explained the A.A. Deputy Commander. " These will take on planes in the normal way. That is, as they come within range."

The discussion continued for some time. Finally the A.A.D.C. announced :

" Well, I think that's all, gentlemen. The barrage will be sent to each of you in the form of an operation order as soon as it is complete. Which I hope will be very soon."

The conference broke up. The Navy fellows stayed behind

to give the A.A.D.C. the information he required about their ships. The Colonel handed in the barrage that had been worked out by his Battery Commanders and was duly thanked. Then he returned to the Fort.

Another two days passed and still no sign of the Luftwaffe beyond the ubiquitous, high-flying " Gunboat Joe." Coming away at mid-day after one of his periodical tours of duty at Gun Operations Room ·the Colonel dropped into the Union Club for a bit of lunch. He joined a table of Gunner officers he knew. With them was a lieutenant from the *Illustrious.*

" How are your people getting on with the repair job ? " asked the Colonel.

" Grand, sir," replied the lieutenant. " The old man says he only wants another twenty-four hours. If nothing happens in the meantime he thinks he'll be able to slip off to-morrow night."

" A pretty big ' if,' " one of the Gunner officers observed.

" Why not ? They've let us alone so far," the lieutenant remarked cheerfully.

" And it's a mystery to me, why," said the Gunner. " It doesn't sound like the Luftwaffe."

" I've got a theory. For what it's worth," said the Colonel.

" What is it, sir ? " asked the lieutenant with interest.

" Well, you are moored in that creek alongside the bastion. I was on top just after you came in, watching the proceedings. I noticed then that the bastion casts a big shadow right across where you are moored. Now, I think that during the past few days these recce planes have been hard at work photographing. They want to make sure exactly where the *Illustrious* is docked so that they can concentrate their entire strength on her. So far, it seems, the photographs haven't told them anything. And I think the reason is that they have all been taken at times when the shadow of the bastion was blotting out the ship."

" That can't go on for ever," one of the others interjected.

" No," agreed the Colonel. " If they happen to take a shot when the sun is in the right direction for them, she'll be dead on the film."

· " And then we shall hear a noise," grinned the lieutenant.

*Illustrious* . . . Luftwaffe. . . . The two words dominated conversation wherever men met in Valetta—in clubs, cafés, shops, streets, and homes. There was every reason for it. The threat of the German bombers seemed to impregnate the very atmosphere they breathed. There was no escaping it. Nor was there any escaping the certainty that, sooner or later, the threat would make way for the blow. The tension was felt even on the gun-sites themselves. For the remainder of the day the Colonel in view of what he had heard of the progress of the aircraft-carrier's repairs, found himself unconsciously ticking-off the fateful twenty-four hours as, one by one, without sign of the Luftwaffe, they slowly passed. Next morning, with less than another twelve hours to go, he acknowledged himself infected with something of the excitement of a gambler watching his horse coming up the straight in a tight finish. Once, in a restless moment, he walked on to the ramparts of the Fort and stood there gazing for a while at the white promontory of Valetta behind which the *Illustrious* lay concealed from view, as if to read the answer to his unspoken question :

" Will she get out before they come ? "

There was something else on his mind also. So far, he had not received the Grand Harbour Barrage from R.A. Headquarters. He knew it meant a big and intricate job. But, on the other hand, any minute might bring the Luftwaffe.

His anxieties on this score were soon to be relieved. A couple of hours before noon a Don R. arrived bringing the barrage in a sealed envelope. It contained the co-ordinates and height at which each of his gun-sites were to fire. Attached to the operation order was a note to the effect :

" This barrage will not be opened unless the *Illustrious* is the target for attack."

Feeling decidedly easier in his mind, the Colonel despatched that part of the barrage which concerned the gun-site at the Three Cities to its Battery Commander, and passed the other on to the Tactical Control Officer in the Command Post. The T.C.O. worked out the range, height and angle of sight for each of the guns and gave it to the Numbers One with instructions that the instant they heard the shout : " Grand Harbour Barrage . . ." all guns were to fire on these lines at a set fuse, whatever else they might be doing at the moment.

The morning passed peacefully. At one o'clock the procession of cooks wended their way over the bridge across the moat with the dixies containing the gun-crews' dinners. In the brilliant sunshine the men sat around the gun-pits devouring slices of beef, boiled potatoes, and cabbage. It being now the season of the *mistral* they had substituted battle-dress for the shorts and shirts of the hotter periods of the year.

The afternoon wore on a little. Bruce, the Gun Position Officer, strolled from the Mess to the Command Post to relieve the subaltern who was his deputy. Everything seemed quiet so he walked into the predictor pit to have a talk with the No. 1. Before he could say two words the loud shout of the telephonist in the Command Post reached his ear.

" Air Observe. . . ."

" Air Observe . . ." yelled the G.P.O. instantly, through his cupped hands.

The Nos. 1 and the layers in the gun-pits jumped to their posts.

" Go to bearing three-two-O," ordered the G.P.O.

The guns swung round to the probable direction from which raiders would come in, and the predictor crew got their instruments on the same rough bearing.

Out of the Mess bolted the Tactical Control Officer with another good meal partially ruined.

" These flaps are doing-in my digestion," he growled, as he dived into the Command Post.

But this time it was to prove something more than a flap.

" Alert . . . Alert . . . Alert . . ." the telephonist began shouting as the A.K. message started to come over from Gun Operations Room.

Outside, the shrill blasts of the alarm whistles echoed throughout the Fort. From all over the island the dismal wail of the warning sirens rose and fell on their ears. Looking over the telephonist's shoulder the T.C.O. saw him pencil-in " 40 plus "—the biggest figure ever, so far—in the column on the A.K. message reserved for the approximate number of raiders. The T.C.O. whistled softly.

" The blitz at last," he said. " This must be the Hun."

A new bearing had come through from G.O.R.

" Go to bearing Nine-O," shouted the Gun Position Officer,

F                                81

and the long, tapering muzzles of the 3.7's once more heavily
traversed the blue sky.

With his eyes fastened to the Telescope Identification the
spotter suddenly descried six planes approaching from the
sea, not in formation, and flying at about 12,000 feet.

" Plane . . ." he roared, adding for the benefit of the
G.P.O. at his side : " Jerries, sir . . . Ju. 88's."

He was overheard by the predictor crew and from here
the news flew into the gun-pits.

" It's the Jerries . . . It's the Jerries . . ." the gunners
told one another.  A subdued excitement gripped them.  At
last the moment they had been expecting for nearly a week !
They had grown a bit weary of high-level I-ti's.  But now
they were taking on the big stuff.  The thrill of it stirred the
pulse of every man of them.

" We'll give 'em *Illustrious*, boys," shouted the sergeant in
No. 3 pit.

" *Illustrious* be b——", exclaimed Smiler, forcibly.  " I
want to give the bastards Hull.  That's my home town.
And the other week they did it a bit of no good."

He glanced over the gun at Doughy, sitting in the other
layer's seat, as serious-faced as ever.

" Best chance you've had yet to make even for your dead
pal Sharman, Doughy," he said.  " A Jerry counts six of
them I-ti's."

But as it happened, Sharman was far from Doughy's mind
at that moment.  He was thinking of Carmela over in Valetta,
and hoping she would be all right.

" Bearing Nine-O, Angle One-Eight degrees . . . Bearing
Nine-One, Angle Two-O degrees . . . Bearing Nine-Two, Angle
Two-One degrees. . . ."

The spotter carried on with his sing-song till he heard the
shouts :

" Height-finder on target . . ."

" Predictor on target . . ."

By now the Ju. 88's had come within range of another,
nearer site, and the guns had taken them on, in the ordinary
way, with height control.  Their white shell-bursts could be
seen uncurling in the air.  Fort Pedro's guns still remained
silent.

Suddenly in the Command Post the telephone began to
speak with a deliberate urgency :

" To all sites, Grand Harbour Barrage . . . To all sites, Grand Harbour Barrage . . ."

The T.C.O. leapt to the doorway and yelled the message to the Gun Position Officer.

" Grand Harbour Barrage ! . . ." roared the G.P.O.'s megaphone.

The barrage opened. For the first time the island defences released their full fury all together. The effect was stunning. The world about the gunners at Fort Pedro seemed to shrink into one colossal noise, with themselves at the core. The guns roared, roared. And their continuous thunder was mixed up with sharp, rending sounds, as if the fabric of the air was being suddenly and violently torn to shreds by scores of pairs of ruthless Titanic hands. They were the screams of the departing shells. And they never ceased. Over Grand Harbour the clear sky magically became a blue canvas dabbed all over with the white tufts of the bursting shells. In the mighty artillery storm the whole Island reverberated and trembled.

Regardless of consequences from shell splinters the Colone and the Adjutant ran out on to the ramparts to watch the sight. The first six twin-engined Ju. 88's had come in from the sea over the Three Cities towards their target. They started in their shallow dive from about 12,000 to 8,000 feet, suddenly dipping their noses, and then released their bombs. From the ramparts the watchers could see them quite plainly falling through the air. Meanwhile, more Ju. 88's were flying in from nearly every direction, converging on the Harbour and unloading their bombs from high above the barrage.

" Here come the Stukas," exclaimed the Colonel.

The Ju. 87's, the dive-bombers, swarms of them, were arriving from the south-east, flying out of the sun so as to make their detection more difficult. With their strange wings and long legs of the fixed under-carriage they resembled a black brood of monstrous pterodactyls resurrected from some prehistoric age. Over the Harbour, at about ten-thousand feet, they stood on their noses, hovered slightly, and then came hurtling down in their screaming dive. Down, down, they dropped to the barrage where, quailing in face of that dreadful storm of steel, some released their bombs. Others dived right through it, not pulling out of their dive till at house-top level, and then amidst a hail of bullets from Bren-guns and machine-guns.

To the roar of the guns was now added the concussion of exploding bombs. From being deafening the noise became stupefying. At least seventy planes were now taking part in the raid. The fury of the barrage appeared to have taken them somewhat by surprise. The Colonel, through his glasses could see them taking evasive action, swerving and dodging till their bombing-run at the last moment. High above the barrage the Hurricane fighters kept on their tails. Already the Stukas showed signs of being badly mauled. One flew away from the island trailing across the sky a long smear of black smoke. Another, with its engine on fire, crashed into the sea. But in the main they continued to face the iron hail without faltering. The Colonel saw one Stuka dive, nose-downwards, right through the barrage, and kept on diving till it hit the sea in a mighty splash.

In the gun-pits the gunners slaved and sweated amid the stench of cordite fumes that grew more choking every minute. If the Stukas did not falter in their efforts neither did the gunners in theirs. The shells were rammed home and despatched at top-speed. Over the Harbour area the sky became so dotted with the shell-bursts as to appear hidden behind one grey cloud. In No. 3 gun-pit at Fort Pedro the ammunition numbers were constantly running backwards and forwards to the main ammunition dump, replenishing supplies. The fuse-setter set the fuses as fast as he could work. The firing became so rapid that very soon the floor of the pit was littered with empty shell-cases. Moving behind the gun in a hurry the sergeant stumbled over a pile.

" Clear some of these bloody things away," he shouted, angrily.

There was no time to stack them up. One of the gun numbers dumped them unceremoniously over the side of the pit.

The Stukas continued to dive and bomb. Across the Harbour, in the direction of the *Illustrious*, great fountains of water every now and then shot up into the air, and set the watchers on the ramparts anxiously wondering. Bombs were falling, too, in Valetta itself, pulverising the limestone buildings they hit. Now and again a thick column of white dust like a tall tree trunk would suddenly sprout from among

the houses, spreading out, as it mounted, into branches and
foliage. After a while there were half-a-dozen of these giant
mushroom growths hanging in the air at the same time. And
behind them, by way of contrast, a pillar of thick black smoke
rose steadily from the burning petrol tank of a plane that
had crashed inland.

In the middle of it all a violent concussion staggered the
occupants of No. 4 gun-pit. Simultaneously a bit of splinter
hit a round in the ammunition rack, and exploded the charge.
There followed a big orange-green flash. The gun-layers
were hurled from their seats and the rest of the crew flung
about the pit in all directions. The loader was killed and
two men wounded.

" Stretcher-bearers . . ." rang out the cry.

From the First-Aid Post in the dry moat gunners hurried
up with a couple of stretchers. They carried away the dead
loader and a man who had his shoulder badly torn. The
third casualty refused to leave the gun. The Colonel ran
over to the pit with the Gun Position Officer to see what had
happened. At first they thought it was a bomb. But a piece
of splinter from a 3.7 shell was picked up in the pit and the
crew of the next gun-pit declared they had caught the glimpse
of a burst just above No. 4 pit. It all pointed to one
conclusion.

" That damned gun-site behind us has caused this mess,"
said the Colonel, with feeling. " They're firing short. We've
caught one of their shells."

He immediately despatched a Don. R. to the battery
commander warning him that in future they were not to fire
over the Pedro site.

In a brief while the gun was in action again.

The Colonel returned to the ramparts and was just in
time to witness one of the thrills of the raid. He saw a
Stuka suddenly dive straight through the barrage with
smoke pouring from it. Right on its tail followed a Hurricane,
guns blazing. The Hurricane, too intent on its prey to
bother about what else happened, shot through the barrage
after it. Afraid for the Hurricane the Colonel yelled to his
gunners to cease fire. His words were lost. Down they came
together, hunted and hunter, lower and lower, till flames
burst out on the Stuka's wing. Satisfied, the Hurricane
made a sharp turn off. The Stuka's wing crumpled up,

85

broke off, and the machine spun headlong into the sea.

Shortly afterwards the gun-crews themselves had a thrill. From across the harbour they saw a raider making direct for them. Their business being the Grand Harbour Barrage, they could do nothing to stop him. They just had to leave him to the attention of the Bren gunners and hope for the best. He flew right over their heads, accompanied by the dud-dud-dud-duddering of the machine-guns, and to everybody's relief dropped his bombs a couple of hundred yards from the gun-site.

The raid lasted about an hour during which Fort Pedro fired something like three hundred and fifty rounds. At the end of that time the Grand Harbour Barrage died away. The "Raiders Passed" signal came. A great silence fell upon the island. A silence that seemed unearthly, unreal, after the tremendous tumult.

In No. 4 gun-pit where the mysterious explosion had occurred, a semi-paralysed gunner asked the sergeant for permission to go to the First Aid Post and have his wound dressed. A piece of shrapnel was lodged between the shoulder-blades and he was completely paralysed above the waist except for the right arm. He had just been able to move this sufficiently to enable him to continue his duty of firing the gun.

"Thought you said you weren't hurt much," said the sergeant, resentfully. "No. I won't let you go and have your wound dressed. I'll see that you're bloody well carried."

"Stretcher-bearer . . ." he roared.

## IX—A BIT OF VICTORY

THE red-faced Battery Commander from the Three Cities gun-site came over to Fort Pedro next morning to discuss with the Colonel certain points in connection with the barrage. He also, according to his unfailing practice, brought the latest news.

"Did they get the *Illustrious* ?" asked the Colonel.

"Twice, sir. But I'm told she's not badly hurt. She must

bear a charmed life. Scores of bombs dropped all round her. Some very near-misses indeed."

" I saw the fountains going up," the Colonel nodded.

" Lucky the barrage was ready just in time," continued the Battery Commander. " That saved her. Even as it was, the dive-bombers did a pretty good job. Time after time they dived right through the barrage. I give the Jerries marks for that, blast them."

" How many down ? "

" Sixteen, so I hear. Ten claims from gun-sites being checked up at H.Q. But I bet we don't get credited with anything like that figure," he added with a laugh. " The R.A.F. will have their say."

" How did the Maltese stand up to it ? "

" Not so bad as might have been expected. They've had nothing like it up to now. There's a hell of a difference between having to put up with a bit of I-ti high-level nonsense and being dive-bombed by getting on for a hundred Ju.'s. I'd say the locals were shaken but not shattered. I'm told Government House is very satisfied with the behaviour of Maltese."

" Much damage ? "

" Lot of houses hit, especially in the Three Cities. So far, fifty-seven men, women and children reported killed. They're still digging. You know that grand old church, Our Lady of Victories, in Senglea ? That's had a bad knock. And they smashed up the convent of St. Dominic, on the opposite side of the creek."

" We had a man killed here, and two wounded," said the Colonel.

" So I heard, sir. Yesterday afternoon. Bad luck," replied the Battery Commander, once more leaving the Colonel marvelling at his talent for knowing everything, almost before it had happened.

That day was marked by nothing more exciting than the re-appearance of the reconnaissance plane " Gunboat Joe." But next day the dive-bombers turned up again. This time their target was not the *Illustrious*. They devoted their attention to the aerodromes, hoping to neutralise them before their next assault on the aircraft-carrier. The attack cost them half-a-dozen planes, and the raiders gained little, despite the vigour and determination of their attacks.

Next day was Sunday, and the Colonel had gone over in the morning on a visit of inspection to the regiment's Dockyard site. A new hut had taken the place of the one demolished when Doughy's friend Sharman had been killed. The Bofors was mounted in the centre of the bare asphalt square inside a circle of double sand-bags, about two and a half feet high.

" Did you hit one the other day ? " asked the Colonel, chatting to the sergeant, who was the detachment commander. " You promised you would."

" I'm afraid not, sir," the sergeant admitted, ruefully.

" You're sure to get another chance soon. So long as the *Illustrious* remains here."

" It wasn't from want of trying," added the sergeant. " D'you know, sir, we fired close on three hundred rounds in that hour. A spell or two like that and we'll run out of gun barrels."

" Air Observe ! . . ." suddenly shouted a gunner from the doorway of the hut.

The gun-layers sprang to their seats on the Bofors. On top of the R.A. Headquarters in Valetta a gunner ran up the warning red flag. And a few seconds later the moaning of the sirens informed the city that their ordeal was about to be renewed.

" Now I'm here I may as well stay and see the show," said the Colonel, stepping into the gun-pit.

Over the Harbour once more came the swarm of Ju. 87's and Ju. 88's. Once more Grand Harbour Barrage bellowed forth with all the intensity of a hundred cracking thunderstorms rolled into one. The Colonel found the din far more deafening than at Fort Pedro. Which was not surprising for, just over the edge of the bastion lay the *Illustrious* herself, and she was defending herself, like a wounded tiger, with the full might of her 4.5 inch guns. The incessant roar of the artillery, and the close screaming of the bombs shattered the atmosphere into an indescribable chaos amid which it seemed necessary to make a strong effort to keep one's bearings. In addition to the concussion of their own shells and the falling bombs the men in the Bofors pit had to sustain the full blast from the heavy guns of the *Illustrious*, which swept up over the edge of the bastion, only a few yards away, and beat and buffeted them like a tornado. Every

now and then the Colonel felt as if his head was in danger
of being jerked off his neck from below.  He discovered it
was due to the webbing-strap of his tin-hat which tugged
hard under his chin whenever the blast caught the brim of
the hat underneath.  He started to adjust the strap to the
back of his head.  On second thoughts he left it as it was.
He didn't fancy the prospect of having the hat blown away
altogether.

The Bofors, swinging round sometimes in a complete
circle, was taking on enemy planes whenever they came into
range.

" Plane ! . . ." roared the detachment commander, pointing out a fresh Ju. 87 that was diving down 'with a scream
over the Harbour.

" Traverse left . . ." the bombardier who was second-in-
command, ordered the layers.  " Down two . . .".   Which
meant that the dive-bomber was heading down the
two-o'clock line on the Bofors' clock-face foresight.

The gun swung round in the direction indicated.

" Lateral zero . . ."

The layers put on the deflection so that their shells should
burst just in the front of the plane.

" On . . . On . . ." yelled the layers almost simultaneously.

" Engage . . ." shouted back the detachment commander,
and before the word was out of his mouth the second-in-
command bellowed : " Fire ! . . ."

The No. 4 pressed his foot on the pedal.

Pom-pom-pom-pom . . .

Pom-pom-pom-pom . . .

The Bofors shells screamed upwards towards the plane,
with the bombardier closely watching the streaks of the
tracers for direction.

" Left to half," he ordered.  And the layers put on the
new deflection.

Again a stream of shells ascended, bursting in the path
of the Ju. 87 but failing to stop it.  The pilot unloaded his
stick of bombs and finished his dive.

" Stop ! . . ." yelled the bombardier, seeing that the
dive-bomber had changed its direction and was now making
off in a level course.  " Nine . . . Right . . . Two . . ."

They managed to get in a couple more bursts and then
came the voice of the detachment commander once more.

" Plane ! . . ."

" Fresh target . . . Traverse right . . . Down Two . . Left one . . ." bawled the bombardier.

And the gun swung through a big arc to engage the newcomer.

Sitting at each side of the gun the two layers plied their traverse and elevating the gear till the plane came within their sights.

" On ! . . ." they yelled.

The No. 4 with a loose rope attached to his ankle so that the sergeant could communicate with him despite the din, again pressed his foot on the pedal.

" Pom-pom-pom-pom . . . Pom-pom-pom-pom . . . " stuttered the Bofors, in its characteristic rhythm.

" On ! . . . On ! . . . the gun-layers kept yelling, as they tracked their quarry through the air.

And each time the No. 4 pressed his foot on the pedal. Without a pause the loader thrust fresh clips, containing four-rounds apiece, into the magazine. Kneeling down beside the boxes a couple of ammunition numbers augmented by the Colonel, who had no desire to remain merely an onlooker at such a juncture, handed him up supplies as fast as he could feed the gun.

Crouched behind the sand-bags the Colonel saw the sky just in front of the gun-pit streaked with the pale phosphorescent lines of the glowing tracers as they sped towards their targets. Cutting across these at all angles, making fantastic geometrical patterns, were the tracers from the eight- and twelve-barrelled pom-poms of the *Illustrious*, streaming in broken rods from over the edge of the bastion like a whitish rain, only going up instead of coming down. Through this curtain darker, heavier objects could be distinguished. They were bombs descending, from the Junkers.

Suddenly the Colonel huddled himself into the corner of the pit, dragging the sergeant with him. A heavy bomb was falling direct on to the gun-site.

The pair held their breaths as it whined down. Fascinated, they watched it, nerving themselves for the explosion. But the explosion did not come. Instead they saw the bomb literally bounce on the asphalt surface of the gun-site and come to rest in a corner.

" A miracle," thought the Colonel, with an uneasy glance

in its direction. In that unexpected moment of relief he did not find speech come readily.

" Here comes another," exclaimed the sergeant, and once more they braced themselves for the shock.

Again no explosion. The bomb bounced about like its forerunner and landed in the opposite corner of the site. This time the pair of them simply stared at one another, both bereft of words befitting such an occasion. The Colonel had to struggle against an irresistible urge to mop his brow.

Meanwhile the Bofors had continued its rapid firing. The crew, so busy with their own job, hardly noticed the special menace of those few seconds. Over the Harbour the air was still dark with planes. They appeared far more numerous than on the previous occasion. But the Colonel noticed they did not seem to be quite so daring as before. Evidently Grand Harbour Barrage had already taken the edge off their appetite. They broke formation quickly in order to bother the gunners, and fewer displayed an inclination to dive right through the barrage.

There was a terrific explosion that shook the gun-pit but did no further harm. The two bombs on the site had exploded simultaneously.

" Plane ! . . ." suddenly shouted the sergeant at the top of his voice, pointing up into the air.

A Ju. 87, coming out of its dive only about 500 feet up, was flying across the site, practically overhead. The layers swung the Bofors on to it, eyes glued to their sights.

" On ! . . ." they shouted together.

The No. 4 trod hard on the pedal. A stream of shells flew in the direction of the plane. Immediately it seemed to falter. Flames burst from the fuselage. A dark object detached itself from the machine and dropped straight for the gun-pit.

" Bomb ! . . ." yelled the sergeant.

The gun-layers involuntarily put up their arms to shield their heads and the rest of the crew flung themselves flat by the sides of the pit. There followed a whizz, a crash. But no explosion.

" Look ! " exclaimed one of the men, breaking the momentary silence that ensued. " They've thrown their bloody gun at us."

There in the gun-pit lay the Ju. 87's machine-gun with

magazine attached, the whole thing complete except that the firing handle had been shot off.

"Well, sergeant, I think you can fairly claim that one as yours," said the Colonel.

"I think so, too, sir," the sergeant replied, delighted. "I swore I'd get one."

He began examining the machine-gun. "Can we keep this gun as a trophy, sir," he asked. "I can get it mended by the artificer and we'll have it mounted. It'll come in handy against low-fliers."

He broke off abruptly. "Look out, everybody," he roared.

Another bomb was screaming down on top of them.

"The third," thought the Colonel. "This is going to end things." And in those few seconds he was a little surprised to find himself regarding his approaching extinction so philosophically.

Huddled down in the gun-pit the men awaited their fate. They heard the bomb hit the asphalt. A second later it burst, rocking the foundations of the very earth. But it left them and their gun very much alive. The Colonel who had given himself up for dead three times in the last quarter of an hour shook himself like a retriever emerging from a cold dip.

At last, after about three-quarters of an hour, the raid ended. The dive-bombers droned away back to Sicily. Grand Harbour Barrage ceased, leaving the air like an alien solitude. The red flag in the roof of the R.A. Headquarters was hauled down. The flocks of pigeons that, as usual, had whirled round and round in agitated flight over Valetta throughout the firing, settled down on the roof-tops in peace. Hundreds of cartridge cases littered the floor of the Bofors pit.

The Colonel walked to the edge of the bastion to see what had happened to the *Illustrious*. He was very relieved to find her undamaged. Groups of Navy gunners, tin-hats over their white anti-flash cowls, stood round the guns enjoying a smoke and a breather. At the foot of the pom-poms the little, brass empty cartridge cases were heaped in thousands.

He moved away to his car, still hardly acclimatised to the unnatural silence.

Bad news awaited him when he returned to Fort Pedro. There had been another explosion in No. 4 gun-pit, the circumstances being exactly similar to those on the previous occasion. Again, one man killed and two wounded.

"What, a second time !" The Colonel went off at full-cock. "Blast that bloody gun-site over there. What the hell are they playing at ! . . . I sent them strictest injunctions not to fire over Pedro."

"They didn't, sir," said the Gun Position Officer. "It's ourselves. We've discovered it's a premature from either No. 1 or No. 2 guns. Probably due to a faulty fuse. For the purposes of the barrage we have been firing over one another at a very low quadrant elevation. So a premature from One or Two might easily burst over Three or Four gun-pit."

"Unbelievable," commented the Colonel. "It was a ten-thousand to one chance against it happening once. And a million to one against a repeat."

Later on, meeting the Colonel in the Mess, the Gun Position Officer said exuberantly :

"It seems the gunners have had a good day, sir. Knocked down about ten. Our telephonist has been listening-in and heard the reports from other gun-sites to G.O.R."

"Pretty difficult considering all the firing, for a site to claim a kill with any certainty," remarked the Colonel. "But there's one for us there can be no dispute about. I saw it with my own eyes on the Dockyard site."

That evening, when dusk was falling, the Colonel walked out alone on the ramparts for a quiet pipe before dinner. Reviewing the events of the day he came to the conclusion that it had provided him with the hottest half-hour or so of his life. He drew hard at his pipe as he recalled the sensations he had experienced when those three 750-lb. bombs dropped on the Bofors site.

"Fate's a damn funny thing," he mused. "A million to one chance over there, and I'm alive to tell the tale. A million to one chance at almost the identical moment here, and there's a man dead."

His thoughts broke off. He removed the pipe from his teeth and stared over the darkening waters towards Valetta. There, from behind the tongue of Fort St. Elmo, a flat, ungainly shape, like a thick shadow, was stealing steadily out into the open sea.

The *Illustrious* . . .

93

He gazed at her, fascinated.  He remembered the evening, not so long ago, when he had stood on that exact spot and watched the crippled ship laboriously making its way to sanctuary.  He remembered the solemn hush on the quay when the wounded were taken off.  He remembered the shell-shocked faces . . . And now the *Illustrious* was boldly setting forth upon the waters once more, firm, solid, and unconquered.  And her enemies had vainly sacrificed thirty-nine planes, to say nothing of the many that had crashed in the sea out of sight and were not counted.  And his guns had helped . . .

The Colonel watched till the night had swallowed her up.

" There goes a bit of victory," he said cheerily to himself.

# PART II

---

PETER, the Battery Commander at the regiment's other gun-site on the far side of the Grand Harbour was living right on top of his reputation. He had arrived on one of his periodical visits to the Mess at Fort Pedro and, as the Adjutant put it, was " earning his keep " by regaling the company with a budget of latest Service scandal and inside information, all acquired by Peter through his usual mysterious infallible channels long before it became common property in Valetta.

Peter possessed a sense of the dramatic. It was this that led him, half-way through dinner, to look up from his slice of fried pumpkin and remark, without previous introduction :

" I wonder how the battle's progressing."

" What battle ? " queried the Colonel, pricking up his ears.

" Convoy attacked in the Narrows, sir," said Peter coolly. " Torpedo-bombers and E-boats. Quite a big affair, I'm told. Lasted two days already, and still wasn't over when I left Valetta a couple of hours ago."

" Any casualties ? " asked the Colonel.

" A destroyer sunk. The *Fearless*."

" Damn ! I've got pals on her," exclaimed the Adjutant. " We all had a slap-up dinner at the Union Club last time she docked here."

" Well, you may have another," said Peter cheerfully. " I'm informed there are lots of survivors. . . . The *Manchester* got a bad knock, too, sir. Had to put back to Gib. We've shot down several bombers and the *Hermione* rammed an Italian submarine. It's been pretty hot."

" What about the convoy ? " asked the Colonel.

" One torpedoed so far, sir. Last news I had was that she was still afloat, but in a bad way. A grain ship, I'm informed."

" I hope she manages to stay on top," said the Colonel. " Grain is just what the Island is badly in need of."

95

" And mail, too, sir," added the G.P.O. " I'm starving
for news from home. We haven't had any letters for God
knows how long."

" If the mail has kept afloat we'll soon know about it,"
said Peter. " The convoy should be in some time to-morrow."

" There'll be a spot of excitement among the natives
down at the Harbour," observed the Adjutant. " They
haven't had the smell of a convoy for ages."

" Not since we got pushed out of Crete," the G.P.O.
asserted.

It was the last week in July and during the six months
that had elapsed since the Luftwaffe's vain attack on the
aircraft-carrier *Illustrious* in Grand Harbour the War had
been big with events affecting in diverse ways the fortunes
of the defenders of Malta. In the early part of the year the
Island had played its stout part in the offensive by Wavell
that resulted in the destruction of Mussolini's African legions
and the conquest of Cyrenaica. During all this period the
Luftwaffe continued their ferocious assaults on the shipping
in the Harbour, and also made desperate attempts to blot
out the scanty aerodromes on the Island. They paid dearly
for whatever success they achieved in this direction. On
one occasion alone the ack-ack gunners enjoyed a field-day
and shot down ten enemy bombers during a single raid.
This apart from another dozen destroyed by our own
Hurricanes which fought with the odds twelve to one against
them. But the pressure of the Germans, if anything,
hardened. The attacks persisted by night as well as day.
They lit up the Island with flares attached to parachutes,
an unpleasant novelty for the inhabitants. More terrifying
still, they dropped parachute mines that sometimes drifted
inland in the darkness and exploded with devastating results
in the heart of Valetta itself. The ack-ack gunners on Fort
Pedro became quite adepts at shooting out the flares and
exploding the mines in mid-air.

As April approached the blitz intensified. Across the
Mediterranean, in Tripoli, Rommel was preparing to strike
back at Wavell. And the Luftwaffe were making it their
business to see that Malta should be so battered and beaten
as to be rendered useless as a base for any material inter-
ference with his preparations. In April the blow came.
Rommel flung his Afrika Korps upon the meagre British

forces in Cyrenaica and drove them back till all that remained of Wavell's Libyan conquest was the hazardously-held port of Tobruk.

And then to the surprise, and relief, of everyone on the island the activities of the Luftwaffe began to diminish visibly. By the end of April it was patent that they were being withdrawn from Sicily. Their exit was as sudden as their entrance three months before. Left only with the high-flying Regia Aeronautica to continue against, Malta—gunners, airmen and civilians alike—enjoyed a well-earned breathing space. They had no idea how long it would last. Nor why it had happened at all. That was quite a mystery. And it remained a mystery to the vast majority till the German onslaught upon Russia the following June shed some light on the subject.

For three months, then, Malta had basked in a spell of comparative calm. After their experiences of the Spring the inhabitants troubled little about the few furtive Italian raids that marked these summer months. And, more important, Grand Harbour became once again an effective naval base.

Peter, the Battery Commander who knew everything, proved correct in his forecast of the arrival of the convoy. Next morning half the population of Valetta gathered on the bastions and quays, to cheer the warships of the escort as they steamed victoriously into Grand Harbour. The fleet of merchantmen followed later in the day with, miraculously, the torpedoed grain ship amongst them.

That same afternoon the sergeant of No. 3 gun on the Pedro site ducked his head and entered the low dug-out where, away from the glare of the sun, three or four members of the gun-crew were dozing-off the effects of a hearty dinner.

" Here. . . You, Smiler . . . You, Doughy . . .", he shouted.

The men addressed shook themselves out of their drowse.

" You two are detailed for a loading job," continued the sergeant. " You got to go down to the Dockyard with Driver Harris and a Matador to help load stores from this convoy just in."

" When ? " asked Smiler.

" Leave here at seven o'clock."

" What we got to do when we get there ? "

G                                    97

" Report to the R.A.S.C. captain. You'll get your orders from him. All the other gun-sites are sending a vehicle. Looks as though there's some hurry."

The sergeant disappeared and the occupants of the dug-out settled down again to resume their interrupted doze.

Punctually at seven o'clock Smiler and Doughy passed through the gates of the Fort. On the road outside, the lorry was drawn up waiting for them. The driver had taken the handles off the door and was now busy removing the front mudguards.

" What's the idea ? " inquired Smiler.

" Economy," replied the driver, grimly. " I want to save the price of a packet of cigarettes out of my pay. I've already been docked three times in the last month for damaged mudguards."

" Why ? Can't you drive straight ? "

" It's them blasted narrow-gutted alleys down by the Dockyard they call streets," replied the driver, with feeling. " D'you know what clearance I've got in some of 'em ? Inch and a half. . . . You got to be able to drive pretty straight to do that. *And* in the dark ! . . . Suppose I happen to dent a mudguard. I go before the Court of Inquiry. Of course, it's always my careless driving. They stick me for the damage. I'm fed up with it. That's why I'm taking all this trouble now."

The driver's grievance burned so fiercely in him that it fired Smiler to sympathy, and he volunteered to lend a hand in removing the mudguards. When the operation was completed the three of them climbed into the lorry and rumbled away down the Melita Road towards Valetta.

After proceeding for some time in silence Smiler turned to Doughy who was sitting beside him in the rear of the driver.

" You got anything pressing on your mind ? " he demanded.

" Why ? " asked Doughy.

" Only because you're saying nothing louder than usual," said Smiler.

Doughy regarded him solemnly for a moment or two, seemed about to open his mouth, but remained as dumb as before. Smiler, knowing his Doughy by now, did not persist. In the past six months an intimacy had developed between the pair which though it could hardly be dignified by the name of friendship, nevertheless had a deeper foundation

than the conventional run of barrack intimacies. Smiler
thought Doughy "a queer bloke," but liked him. Doughy
understood this and liked Smiler back. Needless to say
Smiler provided all the opportunities for whatever develop-
ment had taken place in their intimacy. Nothing would
have happened had it depended on the inarticulate, reticent
Doughy. With the other men on the gun-site his relations
remained the same as they had always been. Smiler was
the only one to whom he felt in any way drawn. And Smiler
himself was far from being a second Sharman. He made no
claim to the gift, possessed by Doughy's dead friend, of
interpreting silence aright, and understanding half-matured
thoughts before they had been shaped into speech. His was
a brisker style that Doughy, with his slow-moving mind and
heavy temperament, sometimes found a strain.

Despite all Smiler's well-meant efforts Doughy would most
probably still have been floundering in the bottomless pit
of loneliness into which Sharman's death had plunged him
over a year before, but for the happy accident of Carmela
Camilleri. It was the black-eyed Maltese dance-girl whom
Doughy had summoned up courage to track down in the
air-raid shelter in Valetta after serving his sentence in the
"Glass House," who had taken the place of Sharman. It
was Carmela who now divined his vague unspoken thoughts
with an instinct as sure as Sharman's. It was Carmela who,
spurred doubtless by the paucity of her English, during the
past twelve months taught herself to interpret his broody
silences when they were sauntering about the Valetta streets
on a twenty-four hours' pass. It was Carmela who had
gradually obliterated the poignancy of Doughy's regret for
the lost Sharman till he was now sometimes ashamed to
recall how faint the memory of his dead friend had become.
And it was Carmela who was engrossing Doughy's mind at
this very moment as he sat beside Smiler in the back of the
Matador on the way to Valetta.

After entering the city the lorry turned off the road to the
right down a steep narrow street leading to the dockyard
area. They progressed slowly through still narrower streets
where the sides of the Matador were almost scraping against
the walls of the houses.

"There you are . . . What did I tell you ? " shouted the
driver triumphantly over his shoulder.

They drove on to the dockside near the Harbour entrance and took their place in a long line of Army lorries which were loading up in turn and driving off. The escort of war-ships had sailed away to rejoin the Mediterranean fleet and out in the Harbour itself the merchantmen of the convoy road at anchor on the deep blue water surrounded by a fleet of lighters into which their cargoes were being unloaded—food stores, gun barrels, ammunition, and aviation spirit. The lighters conveyed their cargoes to the wharves where the lorries awaited them. When it came to the Matador's turn they found their load consisted of boxes of 3.7 shells. An R.A.S.C. sergeant came along with a list, checked up on them, and gave the driver his destination. It was a supply depot about eight miles distant from Valetta in the countryside.

"Come back here when you've dumped that lot and stand by for some more loading first thing in the morning," the sergeant ordered.

It was dark when they returned to Valetta. An air-raid was in progress and occasionally they heard the explosion of a bomb amid the heavy roar of the gunfire. They picked their way at a snail's pace through the narrow streets near the dockyard which were utterly deserted, the inhabitants having fled to the air-raid shelters. As the Matador grated through the gullies the driver was loudly congratulating himself on his sagacity in removing the mudguards, and continually glancing over his shoulder for approbation.

"You look where you're going or you'll bash her nose in," Smiler admonished him. "And me and Doughy here always tell the truth at Courts."

This time they drove right up to Fort St. Elmo at the sea end of the Harbour where, after having some food, they wrapped themselves up in blankets in the rear of the lorry and dropped off to sleep.

The sudden roar of gun-fire awakened them. It was just before dawn and the guns were those of Fort St. Elmo where they were parked. Thinking it only another visit from the Italian bombers they looked out of the back of the vehicle into the sky to discover the direction of the shell-bursts. To their surprise there was nothing to be seen.

"Queer," exclaimed Smiler. "Where's the stuff going ? And look at the searchlights."

The vault of the sky was quite dark. All the beams of the searchlights seemed to be concentrated on the surface of the sea just beyond the Harbour. The guns of Fort St. Elmo continued to thunder.

" That's not ack-ack fire," said Smiler, after listening a moment. " They're those R.M.A. coast guns . . . Six-pounder quick-firers. You can't mistake 'em."

Crowds of excited Maltese children began to swarm from the dockyard area alleys, running towards the edge of the bastion, shouting and gesticulating. Smiler jumped from the lorry.

" Come along, Doughy," he cried. " Let's investigate. P'raps it's the invasion."

The flattened beams of the searchlights were busy roving over the surface of the dark waters which every now and again was illuminated more vividly by the red flash of a bursting shell. The coloured streaks of tracer bullets from the shore batteries carved the black background of the sky into weird geometrical patterns. Just as Smiler and Doughy reached the sea-wall they saw a vessel resembling a large edition of a speed-boat, but equipped with bridge and gun turret, dart out of the obscurity, a mile and a half out to sea, and race towards the Harbour. A searchlight caught and stuck to her. The quick-firers at Fort St. Elmo roared. There was a big flash in which the vessel seemed to disintegrate, bits and pieces of her shooting up into the air in all directions. Then a column of smoke.

" Direct hit," remarked Smiler, cheerfully. " That's an E-boat. I bet they're trying to torpedo the convoy."

" Smiler, I'm thinking of getting married," was Doughy's response.

It was as though under cover of all the din and destruction around a spring had suddenly been released enabling him to unburden himself of the load that had been uppermost in his mind all day. At first the full import of his companion's surprising confidence did not register with the bombardier. His attention was far too absorbed by the drama out at sea.

" Look . . . There's more of 'em . . . Six . . ." He broke off abruptly and gave Doughy a quick glance. " What was that you said just now ? " he demanded.

" I've made up my mind to marry Carmela," said Doughy, to whom the E-boat attack seemed a very secondary affair compared with the weighty matter occupying his thoughts at the moment.

Smiler had no time to digest this piece of information before his attention was diverted seawards once more. The six shadowy E-boats, slipping through the water very fast and throwing up fountains of spray, seemed to be manœuvring for positions outside the Harbour, undeterred by the fire of the coastal batteries. Suddenly Smiler saw a little dark object dart forward. It looked like a torpedo with a man riding it. With shells bursting around it the torpedo shot through the water at a terrific speed, aiming straight for the two-arched bridge at the Harbour end of the Mole. Then, unexpectedly enough, torpedo and rider parted company. Smiler caught glimpses of him bobbing about on top of the churned-up water in a sort of bucket seat. The torpedo sped on without deflection. There came a terrific explosion, a big orange flash that momentarily lit up the Harbour, and one end of the bridge collapsed into the water, effectually blocking the channel.

"Look at that poor bastard waiting for an E-boat to come and pick him up," laughed Smiler, pointing out the figure in the bucket seat. "What a hope."

Doughy gave an assenting nod. His preoccupied manner reminded Smiler of other matters.

"You're being a bloody fool, Doughy," he said. "Who put this idea of getting married into your head? Carmela, I bet."

"No. It wasn't Carmela. I thought it out myself."

"Well, it doesn't do you any credit," returned Smiler. "Besides, I don't believe it was your own idea. If it wasn't Carmela it was them relations of hers. You wouldn't be the first British soldier in Valetta caught like that."

The battle with the E-boats was now at its height. The twin six-pounder quick-firing guns of the Royal Malta Artillery at Fort St. Elmo had got the range of the enemy ships and were blowing them out of the water one by one. A squadron of Hurricanes joined in the fray. They flew low over the sea raking the decks of the E-boats with their machine-guns. A second human torpedo, making another attack on the Harbour entrance received a direct hit and exploded with all the force of a mine, throwing up a great column of water. Its rider vanished into thin air. The engagement continued 'for half an hour and then the remaining E-boats, pursued by the Hurricanes, retreated towards their covering force of destroyers and cruisers which had stood well out to sea and had taken no part at all in the action.

When the guns of Fort St. Elmo ceased firing and the excitement died down Smiler had leisure once more to bestow on the private affairs of Doughy. He lit a cigarette and offered Doughy one. The dawn was breaking and he could read signs of obstinacy in the solemn face of his companion such as he had never noticed before.

" That bloke 'll never be guided by advice once an idea's fixed in his head," he thought. Aloud he said : " You serious about this marrying ? "

Doughy nodded. " I've made up my mind," he said.

" I know," Smiler exclaimed, with a touch of impatience. " You told me so before. And it's all your own idea. . . . What's wrong with you and Carmela carrying on as you've been doing ? "

" I want things on a more regular footing."

" *You* want," Smiler said scornfully. " You mean, she does." He pitched the end of his cigarette over the sea-wall. " You haven't overlooked the fact that you're going to make things a bit uncomfortable for yourself at the Fort, have you ? "

" How ? "

" Marriages between troops and Maltese girls ain't regarded with too much favour by the high-ups. The Major won't like it. And I'm dead sure the C.O. will hate it."

" They can't stop me," said Doughy doggedly.

" They can't stop you," echoed Smiler. " But they can make you feel all the time that you're not getting a medal for it. The C.O.'s got strong feelings on the subject of mixed marriages. I remember we had a case just before you joined. One of our Bofors gunners. He wanted to get married to a Maltese bit. And the C.O. went to lots of trouble to see that he didn't. Even got the Provost-Marshal to give him one of his man-to-man talks, all to himself."

" What happened ? "

" Bloke came out of his trance in time."

" He never felt like I do about Carmela," Doughy said slowly, after a pause.

" I don't expect there was much difference," Smiler observed with a cynical grin.

But Doughy just then was not thinking of love or anything like it. He was thinking of the gap that Carmela filled in his life, the misery of the spell of loneliness he had endured before he found her, and the lurking dread in his mind lest he should lose her and revert to his former condition. The idea of marrying her had been born of this dread. It was an insurance he was after, first and foremost.

" Look . . . On the end of the Mole . . . What do you say to that ? . . ." suddenly cried Smiler.

A very dripping, bedraggled object wearing a sort of skull-cap, sat perched on the end of the Mole, looking the picture of misery. It was the pilot of the torpedo that had wrecked the bridge. Tired of floating about in the sea waiting to be picked up by E-boats that were themselves floating in pieces on the waters, he had swum to the Mole, clambered up, and now waited, sodden and resigned to be taken prisoner. An R.A.F. rescue launch brought him to Fort St. Elmo. Crowds of Maltese children, booing and hissing, followed him as he was being escorted through the Fort for interrogation. As the little procession passed close to where Smiler and Doughy were leaning against the sea-wall, one of the Maltese gunners, momentarily overcome by his feelings, threw a stone at the prisoner. An officer strode up.

" Why did you do that ? " he demanded angrily.

" He's Italian. I'm Maltese," was the simple reply.

The explanation was not considered good enough and the gunner was marched off to the guard-room.

At the same time a Navy tug came alongside towing a captured E-boat. The entire crew of the vessel lay sprawled across the deck, riddled with machine-gun bullets from a Hurricane. Smiler and Doughy were watching the bodies being lifted ashore when the driver of their lorry sauntered up. They hadn't seen him since the beginning of the attack.

" Time we were moving," he announced. " What happened ? I went back to finish my sleep."

" Nearly the invasion," Smiler replied, drily. " You did wise."

They drove down to Pier Tower wharf where they started to load up again. The rest of the day was occupied in journeys to various gun-sites, dumping gun barrels and ammunition.

It was late in the evening by the time they returned to Fort Pedro. At the Fort itself the gunners had seen little of the attack, though they knew by now that the entire E-boat force had been wiped out. Their own guns had been manned for their invasion task, but had not come into action. , They plied Smiler for details. He briefly described the salient features, including the torpedo attempts on the Harbour.

" Kindergarten stuff," he summed up, contemptuously. " A few I-ti's giving an imitation of surf-riding at Blackpool. Funny, but nothing else to it. I'll tell you something, though, that is serious. Doughy, here, is going to get spliced."

" How's he working his ticket home for that ? " asked a gunner.

" It's his bit over in Valetta," explained Smiler. " I've been telling him what a bloody fool he is."

" Why shouldn't a bloke marry a Maltese if he feels that way ? " demanded Steve the loader. " What haven't they got that the others have ? "

" Nothing," snapped Smiler. " And very likely they've got more. I'm calling him a bloody fool for wanting to get married at all."

" Beer don't suit him. Women may," said Steve. " It's one or the other with a bloke."

" How does he know ? " replied Smiler in disgust. " Has he ever been married before ? " He suddenly turned to Doughy who was lying on his bunk listening vaguely to the discussion of his affairs. " I bet you don't know the most important thing about marriage," he challenged.

" Money ? " suggested Doughy cautiously, after a pause.

" Nearly. But not quite."

" Love ? "

" Cold as ice," Smiler retorted with .scorn. " The most important thing in marriage is whether her relations like you and whether your relations like her. And I know what I'm talking about. If it hadn't been for that I might now be in a munitions factory at home drawing eight quid a week instead of sweating on this bloody island for five-bob a day."

" I haven't got any relations," observed Doughy mildly.

" No. But she has. And lots you haven't seen yet, I'll

swear. And that reminds me. Did they ever invite you to
have a cup ot tea with them ? "

"Yes. First time I met Carmela in the air-raid shelter."

"Did you accept ? "

"Yes."

"Blimey, then you've been sunk from the start," explained
Smiler disgustedly. "Didn't you know ? If you go home
with a Maltese girl and have a cup of tea with her relatives
they regard it as good as an offer of marriage."


## II—THE BATTERY COMMANDER INTERVENES

SMILER, in the weeks that followed, continued to let Doughy
see he regarded him as a bloody fool. Don-Troop, generally
speaking, let Doughy see that they were in complete agreement with Smiler. Steve, the loader on No. 3 gun, went to
great trouble to expound unto Doughy the superiority of
beer to wives as a pastime spread over the years. The teak-
torsoed gunner, who was in the habit of entertaining the
dug-out in the evenings on the mouth-organ with selections
from a vast repertory, made a point of always dropping into
a few bars of "When We Are Married . . ." whenever
Doughy entered.

Despite these kind attentions Doughy's resolution displayed
no signs of weakening. Once having made up his mind to
marry Carmela nothing could budge him. He was now
making up his mind, with his usual slow deliberation, to
approach his Battery Commander on the subject. Doughy,
before acting, always liked to lay a solid foundation of
decision within him, so as to feel certain that nothing on
earth could divert him from his purpose. This accounted for
the pig-headed side of an otherwise quiet, inoffensive
disposition.

Nearly a month passed without the foundation having
solidified sufficient to Doughy's liking. However it was the
Battery Commander himself who saved him from further
delay. In the mysterious way such things do happen, echoes
of Doughy's private intentions permeated from the gun-pits
to the Battery Office.

" Sergeant-Major," said the Battery Commander one morning, " I hear Gunner Baker wants to marry some Maltese girl. Have you heard anything ? What's the strength of it ? "

The Battery sergeant-major had heard very little. But he made the most of what he had heard.

" I did hear, sir, he's been spending his pay on some bar tart in Valetta," he replied.

" Is this the girl he proposes to marry ? "

" Quite likely, sir. Unless he's running more than one."

" I'm surprised," commented the Battery Commander. " He has always struck me as such a sensible, solid fellow."

". First-rate gunner, sir," volunteered the B.S.M.

" It has always remained a mystery to me how he came to lose his stripe." The Battery Commander paused, looked out of the window reflectively, and added :

" There's all the difference between running round with a girl and wanting to marry her."

" Yes, sir," agreed the sergeant-major emphatically.

" I think I'd better see him. He seems too good a young fellow to leave to make a fool of himself."

" When, sir ? "

" This afternoon. Three o'clock. Unless we are in action."

Hence it followed that with no " Air Observe " on for the time being, Gunner Doughy Baker stood respectful and stolid-faced in front of the Major's table in the Battery Office.

" Sit down, Baker," said the Major pleasantly. " I've heard a rumour that you're thinking of getting married. Is that true ? "

At once Doughy was on his guard. He realised that the " uncomfortable " period forecast by Smiler down at the Harbour on the night of the E-boat attack was now about to begin. His solemn face hardened with a slight trace of obstinacy.

" Yes, sir," he replied.

" Is she a Maltese ? "

" Yes, sir."

" I'm sorry to hear that," said the Major.

He rose from his chair and began to pace the room in front of Doughy.

" You know, Baker," he said, adopting his best fatherly manner, " this war isn't going to last for ever. Some time or other you'll be going back to England. Have you considered the problems that will arise then if you have a Maltese wife. Will she want to leave her kith and kin ? You know, the family tie is very strong among the Maltese. They're linked very closely together—sisters, brothers, aunts, uncles, sisters-in-law, mothers-in-law, nephews, nieces. The whole family tribe, in fact. It isn't quite like it is in England where, when you marry a girl, the husband counts before the family. If you marry this girl, when the time comes for you to leave the island she may refuse to accompany you. It isn't an unusual occurrence where troops have married Maltese girls. You must bear that in mind before doing anything rash."

Doughy remained dumb, his eyes fixed on the wall in front of him.

" You're quite a young man," proceeded the Major. " What are you ? Twenty-er . . . ? "

" One, last March, sir."

" Twenty-one . . . Well, you don't want to tie yourself up for life to a girl of foreign blood whom you've married just because of a passing fancy."

" It isn't a passing fancy, sir," said Doughy.

" How old is she ? "

" Eighteen, sir."

" She may be a girl now. But, remember, out here the women age very quickly. Far quicker than English girls. In a few years' time you'll find her looking like a middle-aged woman. All run to fat."

" It isn't looks I'm after, sir," said Doughy, doggedly. He was thinking that if fat and middle-aged looking, Carmela would still be his insurance against loneliness.

" Then there's the question of religion," persisted the Battery Commander. " A most serious problem to be considered. You are C. of E., I suppose."

" Yes, sir."

" And she's a Catholic. Are you aware that any children you may have by her will have to be brought up in the R.C. faith ? Are you aware you'll be asked to sign a declaration to that effect ? "

" I shan't mind that, sir."

" Sticking to your guns, eh ? " said the Battery Commander

with a faint smile. " Well, Baker, I think I've pointed out the most important facts for you to consider before you take any further step. I don't want to see you make a fool of yourself like so many young fellows do. You've got the makings of a good husband for some nice English girl. ' Stick to your own people. Now you go away and think over all I've said, and come and see me again."

" To-morrow, sir ? " asked Doughy.

" Good heavens, no. Take a fortnight . . . Better still, a month. A month won't be too long for such a serious matter."

" Thank you, sir."

" There goes a damn young fool," murmured the Battery Commander to himself as Doughy passed out of the office.

In the Mess that night the B.C. broke the news to the Colonel.

" That Maltese marriage nuisance has cropped up again, sir," he said.

" Who is it this time ? " asked the Colonel, frowning.

" One of the layers on No. 3 gun. Gunner Baker. A virulent case, I suspect. I talked to him in the office for half an hour this afternoon. Without much success, I'm afraid."

The Colonel was looking distinctly put out, as the B.C. expected he would be. Everyone was aware of his deeply-rooted antipathy, for various reasons, towards these mixed marriages between troops and Maltese girls. Especially, he hated the idea of it occurring in his own regiment.

" I sincerely hope your words will have a good effect," he said to the Major. " These marriages are not in the interests of either party. We can't prevent them. But we ought to do everything to discourage them."

" Is it true, sir, that there are over four thousand deserted Maltese wives in the island ? " inquired the Gun Position Officer.

" Very likely. It's some colossal figure, I believe," replied the Colonel. " ' Deserted ' isn't quite the right word, though. What often happens is that a girl marries a troop, or a naval rating, and when the time comes for him to proceed to another station she refuses to leave her relations. So he goes off alone. Some of these wives haven't seen their husbands for years. And never will see them. Meanwhile, they, and their relations, continue living on the island at the expense of the

Army. A very unsatisfactory state of affairs. Of course it only happens among the poorest class of Maltese."

" These lower-class Maltese are intensely proud of making a personal connection with the Army," said the Major. " They like to boast of having a British soldier in the family, even if he is a long way off. It gives them a sort of prestige over the others. Flattering to us, in a way. A sign of patriotism."

" Yes, and it pays," commented the Colonel, drily. " Then there's the religious side of the matter. That's unsatisfactory, too. It isn't only the Army authorities in Malta who don't like these mixed marriages. Their own Archbishop-Bishop himself strongly disapproves. I wish the powers-that-be at home would send us out a ship-load of A.T.S. and W.A.A.F.'s and some more English nurses so as to give the troops a chance of becoming engaged to girls of their own country. That would put a stop to it. I see no other way."

" Well, I've given this fellow a month to think it over. I'll let you know the result, sir," said the Major.

Beset with other duties and responsibilities he had quite forgotten all about the matter when, punctually to the hour and the day, Doughy presented himself at the Battery Office. The sergeant-major knocked on the door of the Major's room.

" Will you see Gunner Baker, sir ? "

" Gunner Baker ? What about ? "

" Says you told him to report to you in a month's time, sir."

" Oh, yes, I remember. Send him in."

The Battery Commander shot a swift glance at Doughy's face as he entered. The solemn features told him nothing.

" Sit down, Baker. I hope you've come to tell me you've thought better of it."

" I still want to marry her, sir."

This time it was the Major's face that hardened slightly. Kid-gloves having failed he considered himself justified in adopting a stiffer attitude. He was not to know that the only thing with power to put the wind right up Doughy was dread of finding himself a victim once more to that devastating sense of loneliness from which Carmela had saved him after the death of Sharman. The Major regarded it as just another unfortunate case of sex infatuation.

" I'm sorry to hear that," he said curtly. " Is it true that this girl is a dance-partner in some Valetta café ? "

" Not now, sir. She was. Only for a bit."

" Where is she now ? "

" At the Regional Protection Office, sir."

" What does she do there ? "

" Looks after the ration cards, I think, sir."

The Battery Commander considered his next step for a moment.

" Are you in any trouble over her ? " he inquired. " If so, tell me frankly. If it is just a matter of money I might be able to arrange to advance you a sum and have it deducted weekly from your pay."

" There's no trouble of that sort, sir," replied Doughy, stolidly.

" You know, Baker," continued the Major, investing his voice with a touch of authority, " I don't like the idea of this marriage at all. I've had a word with the Colonel and he is as anxious as I am that it shall not take place. He will never give his blessing to any man from the regiment marrying a Maltese. He has been stationed in Malta several years and has seen many similar cases. The marriages don't always end satisfactorily. Why not be guided by his long experience and superior judgment ? "

As there was no response from Doughy to this invitation the Major proceeded :

" Of course, there's no compulsion about the matter. You are a perfectly free agent—free to marry whom you choose. What I have said I have said for your own good. Think it over again. But whatever you do decide, let me know before you take any further steps."

" Yes, sir," said Doughy.

Then the Major had another thought . . . the Provost-Marshal.

The Provost-Marshal, a Lieutenant-Colonel of the Marines, occupied a very distinctive place in the life of the island. A former heavy-weight boxing champion, and a man of wide experience and wide sympathies, he was equally popular with the garrison and civil population. It was he who gave lectures to all newly-arrived troops on " the Maltese wives question," and warned them against the peculiar delayed-action effect of the local wine called by the troops " ambeet."

Every evening without fail he was to be found between
6 p.m. and 8 p.m. at the Royal Navy Picket House. Here
he held a sort of Solomon's Court, dispensing widsom to all
comers. Soldiers, sailors and airmen came along to ask his
advice. Wives of Service men brought him their troubles
which might be anything from the spots on the baby's belly
to desertion. He knew everyone in Malta, never forgot a
face, and possessed as part and parcel of his official duties
a photograph album of all the loose women in Valetta known
to be suffering from venereal disease. At night, with his
Master-at-Arms, he paid surprise visits to the cabarets and
dance-halls on the look-out for any faces that figured in his
picture-book.

" What is this girl's name ? " asked the B.C. of Doughy.

" Carmela, Camilleri, sir."

" Address ? "

" She lives in an air-raid shelter, sir."

" Never mind. We can find her at the Regional Office,"
said the Major. " As she has been a dance girl, for your own
benefit it will be just as well to make a few inquiries. I'll
get in touch with the Provost-Marshal who has a great fund
of knowledge about these girls. You can go now. And,
remember, all these things are being done for your own
good."

" Yes, sir," said Doughy, simply.

III—RETURN OF THE LUFTWAFFE

DOUGHY'S progress towards the state of holy matrimony
was destined to provide blessed relief to Don-Troop, and
more especially to his own gun-crew, from their graver
preoccupations during the hectic months that were on their
way. When that time came they found it a welcome diversion
to switch their minds on to the pros and cons of this petty
human tussle after spending twelve or fifteen continuous
hours in the cordite-stinking gun-pits, with bombs bursting
around them, Grand Harbour Barrage roaring, and their
own little world apparently in a state of immediate disinteg-
ration. In those harsh days sleep was their first recreation.

Their second was the discussion of Doughy's affairs. But all this was still to come.

After Doughy's second interview with the Battery Commander a subtle change took place in the general attitude of No. 3 gun-crew towards him. With the single exception of Smiler they ceased to regard him simply as a plain bloody fool. " Misguided " was the most severe criticism passed on him now. This swing-round in his favour was brought about solely by the admiration aroused in all but Smiler for the stout way Doughy was resisting the pressure being brought to bear upon him in the Battery Office to change his mind.

Steve, the loader, who in his off-duty spells bred rabbits in the ' farmyard,' not far from the gun-pits, where the men had erected chicken-houses and hutches of weird and wonderful designs, paid Doughy the compliment of naming his most prolific doe Carmela.

One or two old sweats of the " barrack-room lawyer " type professed to elevate the affair to the level of David and Goliath . . . the humble gunner pitted against the whole weight of the Army Council. They plied Doughy with advice and encouraged him to resist all the B.C.'s blandishments. Whereat Smiler fumed with wrath.

" Don't you listen to them bloody gas-bags, Doughy," he urged. " They're only trying to make a sucker of you. What do they really care whether you marry the girl or not ? "

" They don't count with me," replied Doughy, firmly.

His position was simple. He had made up his own mind and wanted no outside help to make him stick to it.

" That's all right . . . So long as you're not getting the idea into your head that you're a hero instead of a bloody fool," said Smiler with brutal frankness. Mind you, I've nothing to say against Carmela herself, as I've told you before. What beats me is why you want to get married at all. And if the B.C. can stop you I don't care how he does it."

Entering the office one morning in early autumn the Battery Commander noticed a lavender coloured envelope, not too fresh-looking, lying on his table. It was addressed to him. He picked it up, sniffed twice at a faint odour of cheap scent, and drew forth a sheet of lavender notepaper embellished with a pink and blue floral design.

" What's this, Sergeant-Major ? " he laughed. " A valentine ? "

" Don't know, sir. It must have come while I was out."

The Battery Commander commenced to read. His smile vanished.

" Damned young fool, . . . " he muttered.

The letter was brief and read as follows :

> From Gunner Baker, No. 506602, to the Battery Commander, No. 1 Battery.
> Sir,
> After much thought and having given the matter long consideration, I have decided to change from C. of E. to R.C. for the benefit of my conscience.
> I remain,
> Yours obediently,
> HENRY BAKER.

" Benefit of his conscience ! . . ." exclaimed the B.C. to himself with scorn. Aloud he said : " It's a note from Gunner Baker, Sergeant-Major. He wants to change from C. of E. to R.C."

" Why, sir ? "

" See what he says for yourself," replied the B.C., tossing the letter over.

So long had elapsed since his last interview with Doughy that the B.C. had hoped no more was going to be heard about this troublesome marriage. In the meantime he had received a report from the Provost Marshal to the effect that inquiries showed that Carmela Camilleri was quite a respectable girl. Her relations were rather poor people, but also had nothing against them. The girl herself had only been employed as dance partner at the Balmoral for a week, and neither before nor since had taken any similar engagement. Her priest gave her a very good character.

That was all right so far as it went. But it didn't mean that the Major, to say nothing of the C.O., would withdraw opposition to the marriage.

The sergeant-major read the letter and replaced it before the Battery Commander without comment.

" Notepaper supplied by the girl," observed the B.C., fingering it disdainfully. " No troop would be such a pansy as to buy such gaudy stuff. And I'm willing to bet, Sergeant-Major, she was hanging over his shoulder when he wrote the letter.  Probably in some café . . . Send over to the gun-pit for him.  I'll tackle him at once."

The gun-crew all guessed what was afoot when an orderly announced :

" Gunner Baker wanted at the office immediately."

" Keep your tail up, Doughy," somebody shouted.

" Never mind about your tail," said Smiler.  " You keep your lugs wide open and soak up the good advice."

" I thought you'd given up the idea of marrying, Baker," the Major began when Doughy appeared, stolid-looking as ever.

" No, sir."

The Major tapped the lavender-coloured letter.

" What's all this about ? "

" I want to become R.C., sir."

" Why ? "

" I've studied things, sir, and as my girl is R.C. I think it best I should become R.C. too, for the sake of the children."

" But you say here, ' for the benefit of your conscience '. That's not quite the same thing.  You're contemplating a very drastic step, Baker.  And one that isn't necessary. I should be sorry to see this marriage go through.  But if it does, there's no reason why you should change your faith. You can marry the girl and still remain C. of E.   You understand that, don't you ? "

" I've seen my girl's priest, sir.  We had a long talk together. He says that me not being R.C. we can't get married before the altar.  My girl doesn't want to be married in the vestry, sir.  She doesn't like the idea of it."

" So you've decided to change on that account.  Your own faith doesn't seem to have troubled you much."

" There don't seem to me much difference between the two, sir."

" It's not so simple as all that.  You haven't found out yet.  I ought to tell you that the Archbishop-Bishop of Malta, who is head of the R.C. Church here, has himself expressed the opinion that men who change their religion just to get married are not likely to make very devout Catholics."

There was a pause.  A new thought dawned in the Battery

Commander's mind. He came to the conclusion that possibly it would serve the end he had in view if he allowed matters to take their course without further discussion. Supposing the gunner was eventually received into the Catholic Church it would take some months. And during that time there was always the chance he would fall out with the girl. Without the clue to Doughy's real motive the Battery Commander still regarded him as the victim of an infatuation that, sooner or later, would wear itself out.

While considering the matter from this new angle he suddenly heard from outside the shrill blasts of the Command Post whistle denoting an air-raid. Soon the guns were in action. The concussion of the firing shook the walls and windows of the office. The Battery Commander was more conscious of the gunfire than he otherwise would have been because for some days things had been very quiet at the Fort, with hardly a raid at all.

He turned his attention once more to Doughy.

" I am to assume, then, that you have definitely made up your mind to change to R.C. ? " he queried.

" Yes, sir," replied Doughy, firmly.

" I want to be quite certain on the point because I shall have to send copies of your letter to the C. of E. Assistant Chaplain-General of the Forces 'and to the R.C. Chaplain of the Forces. They will each want to interview you."

" Yes, sir."

" I· may as well warn you that one will want very good reasons why you are quitting C. of E., and the other very good reasons why you want to become R.C. It won't be sufficient just to say because you want to get married."

" What sort of reasons, sir ? " Doughy inquired, without a break in his poker-face.

" Well, I imagine you'll have to show good cause why you have suddenly discovered that C. of E. no longer satisfies your spiritual needs and R.C. does. This won't be a quick business, you know. If your application goes through you'll then have to undergo a certain amount of instruction which the R.C. Chaplain will arrange for, before you can be received into the R.C. Church.

" What sort of instruction, sir ? "

" Religious instruction. Something I believe, corresponding to a Confirmation Class in the Anglican Church."

" I've never been confirmed, sir," said Doughy.

The Battery Commander stood up indicating that the interview was at an end.

" You'll find out all about it in due course," he said. " And if everything goes well you'll be R.C. in a matter of three months or so."

" Thank you, sir."

Doughy had been gone about ten minutes, and the firing outside had ceased for some time, when the Gun Position Officer coming off duty entered the office.

" What was the little fuss outside ? " enquired the Major, casually.

" Nothing, sir, to the fuss that is on its way," replied the G.P.O.

The grim note in his voice caused the Major to lift his eyebrows questioningly.

" Meaning ? "

" Guess what we were shooting at, sir," the G.P.O. continued. " A recce plane. A little devil with a yellow nose. . . . An Me. 109, sir."

The Battery-Commander whistled.

" The Luftwaffe back again ! . . . There have been rumours. Well, it's good-bye to our little holiday, and all that. About five months, isn't it ? I must confess it has been pleasant enough while it lasted."

" I don't envy them their reception, sir."

" No. The island bristles with guns now," said the Major, thoughtfully. " Grand Harbour Barrage must be twice as powerful as it was when they were here before. They're in for a hot time. So, by the way, are we . . ."


## IV—THE STORM BURSTS ANEW

THE Luftwaffe lost no time in making its presence felt. The " hot time " prophesied by the Battery Commander soon became the perquisite of all—garrison and civilians alike. Their consolation lay in giving back as good as they got. Once more the Hurricanes fought their fight against desperate odds. Once more, day and night, the streets of

Valetta echoed the crash of falling bombs and falling buildings. Once more the gunners slaved and sweated in the gun-pits. And once more did Grand Harbour Barrage blast the upper air with a fury before which the most intrepid of the Luftwaffe pilots had good reason to quail. They did, in fact, pay much more respect to the barrage than had been the case with their predecessors on the first encounter during the attack on the *Illustrious*, eight months previously. The memory of their deadly reception on that occasion had evidently bitten in deep. Besides, as the Battery Commander had said, the weight of the barrage had vastly increased during those intervening months.

Nevertheless, the flow of life in Valetta, which had resumed a more or less normal tenor during the Italian interregnum, again became sadly broken and disjointed. The afternoon crowds in the Strada Stretta thinned to a shadow of their customary selves. A fresh exodus of refugees and household chattels to the outlying villages set in. Scores of the little shops in the Strada Reale put their shutters up and, as it happened, were not to take them down again for many a dark month. Traffic dwindled away and the passing of ambulances became more conspicuous. And in the air-raid shelters the rosaries were told with more than common fervour. Grimly the city prepared itself for fresh sacrifices. There was alarm and uneasiness among the population. But nothing of the widespread dreads that had gripped most hearts on the first appearance of the Luftwaffe in Sicily. Having weathered that storm the Maltese had confidence in their powers, and in the powers of the island defences, to face the new onslaught without faltering. Nothing, they thought, could be worse than those concentrated attacks when the *Illustrious* was refitting in Grand Harbour. Time was near at hand, ready to disillusionise them.

At Fort Pedro the gunners settled down to the new conditions and, to begin with, enjoyed the excitement of having another go at the Luftwaffe after the monotony of months of potting at high-flying I-ti's.

Towards the end of an afternoon late in autumn the Command Post telephonist, sitting with earphones on before his instrument, called to the Gun Position Officer:

" Wanted by Gun Operations Room, sir."

The G.P.O. took the 'phone.

" Pedro gun-site here," he said.

" Gun-night to-night," was the reply.

It was the duty-officer at G.O.R. letting the gun-sites know that no night-fighters would be up that night so, in the event of a raid the guns could engage targets with nothing to hinder them.

The night drew on, lovely, warm, with no wind and no clouds, and a heaven brilliant with stars. It was nearly eleven o'clock before they got an " Air Observe." When the raid did develop it proved to be one of those assorted affairs that were always a tax upon the temper of the Tactical Control Officer whose job it was to work out the plots.

The Gun Position Officer darted up to have a glance at the plotting board. The T.C.O. was struggling to work out, at one and the same time, the plots of six little separate raids, totalling up fifty aircraft, which were flying in from six different directions.

" We'll take the one that seems to concern us most," decided the Gun Position Officer. " This looks like it."

It was a " ten plus " affair coming in from the sea on a course that would probably bring it over Sliema to Valetta.

" They may, of course, turn and attack from inland," the G.P.O. reflected. " But I think we'll chance it."

He ran out into the darkness and shouted to the guns :

" Go to bearing Six-O degrees," this being the rough direction of the approaching planes.

Back at the Tactical Control Officer's elbow he saw that new figures had come through from Gun Operations Room concerning the plot.

" That's ours all right," he said, and disappeared outside again.

Swiftly finishing his calculations the T.C.O. shouted the information through the door of his dug-out.

" Bearing, Two-O . . .  Angle, One-O degrees . . ."

Outside in the darkness the G.P.O. relayed the orders to the Command Post crew. Shadowy figures grouped them-selves around the predictor, height-finder and telescope identification. A faint blue glow, like a will-o'-the-wisp hovered in the predictor pit. It was the predictor dial, illuminated internally by a small electric bulb. Otherwise all was darkness, as it was in the gun-pits, too, except for a similar pale blue glow on the gun dials lit in the same way.

Besides being a gun night it was also a searchlight night. Dozens of them, all over the island, were busy searching the dark places among the stars. Their long beams continually opened wide apart and closed together again as if the silver blades of several pairs of gigantic scissors were at work cutting the stuff of the night sky into segments. Watching them, on the ramparts of the Fort stood the Colonel and the Adjutant, the former, who had been just about to turn in when the raid started, quaintly attired in striped pyjamas and a tin-hat.

Gradually in the silent night the drone of the invisible raiders began to sound menacingly as they drew nearer to the island. First came a wave of " pathfinders " which flew in from the sea and circled Valetta, going backwards and forwards several times while they made certain of their position. Occasionally from high overhead in the pied ceiling of the sky came the vibrant zoom of an engine as its pilot, taking evasive action to escape the attentions of a searchlight, went into a shallow dive. All around the guns of the ground defences roared into action, some firing a barrage over Valetta, others taking on illuminated targets. The guns of Fort Pedro were engaged in the latter task.

When the raiders had made sure they were over Valetta they commenced to drop flares. These descended from a height of about eight thousand feet, dangling on the end of parachutes, and looking like enormous incandescent lamps. The Colonel counted quite a score of them burning in the air at the same time, all dropping so slowly that they almost seemed to be suspended in the sky for good. They lit up Valetta, the Harbour, Fort Pedro, and the neighbourhood with a vivid bluish light, like a hard, cruel, artificial daylight.

The Colonel on the ramparts wriggled his shoulders in discomfort.

" Upon my word," he declared, " this glare makes me feel in peril of being arrested for indecent exposure. I'm damned if I don't feel quite naked. I suppose it's having nothing on but pyjamas. I think I'll go inside and put on an overcoat. I'll feel more comfortable."

" You won't, sir," the Adjutant assured him. " I feel just the same as you do. And I'm wearing battle-dress. It's exactly like being X-rayed, isn't it ? "

" I hope to God they can't see me up there as plainly as I fancy they can," laughed the Colonel.

Amid the deeper note of the big guns could be heard the incessant pom-pom-pom-pom . . . pom-pom-pom-pom . . . of the quick-firing Bofors engaged in the task of shooting out the flares. Soon the sky presented a bewildering picture of variegated lights and colours. Far, far away, the cold white brilliance of innumerable stars. Below the soft greyish patches of the roving searchlights intermingled with the red flashes from the bursting shells of the barrage. Below that, the long white pathways of the searchlights stretching from heaven down to earth. The pale blue incandescence of the slowly dropping flares. And finally the lower sky carved up into all sorts of geometrical shapes by the soaring orange-yellow tracers of the Bofors, which resembled streaks or balls of fire according to the angle of vision.

So far no bombs had fallen. Evidently it was a raid for the purpose of laying mines in the harbour. The Colonel noticed one plane caught momentarily by a searchlight. Immediately a couple of mines attached to parachutes dropped out.

In the midst of his other duties the Gun Position Officer also was keeping a keen look-out for mines. Suddenly he saw one dropping into the sea between Sliema and Fort Pedro.

" Bombardier, take the bearing of that mine," he shouted, pointing it out to the man at the T.I. (telescope identification).

Having received the information the G.P.O. hurried into the Command Post and got through to Gun Operations Room.

" Pedro speaking . . . Mine seen falling, bearing O-Five degrees . . . Time 23.30 hours."

As he turned to leave the Adjutant entered.

" Did you get the bearing of that mine ? If not, I did," he said.

" Thanks," replied the G.P.O. " I've just given G.O.R. the word."

" Fish should be plentiful to-morrow," grinned the Adjutant.

On these mine-laying nights it was one of the jobs of the gun-sites to keep Gun Operations 'Room informed of any mines seen dropped. By comparing the different bearings received, G.O.R. was enabled to plot the approximate position where a mine had hit the sea. This intelligence was passed on to the Navy for the benefit of the mine-sweepers that would go out next morning. Such occasions provided the fishermen and longshoremen of Valetta with much agreeable excitement. Directly a mine was brought to the surface by the Naval men they exploded it by shooting at it with a Lewis gun. Immediately the surface of the sea became white with the bellies of thousands of stunned fish. The fishermen at once rowed out in boats of every description to haul in the easy catch. They were the only people who ever had a good word to say for the raiders! Sometimes notice when mines were to be exploded was published in the *Times of Malta* in advance, as a warning to people. On such occasions boats and crews in hundreds lined up along the beaches of the harbour as if for the start of a mammoth regatta.

The Adjutant had just regained the ramparts when a bomb whistled down. It was the first and only bomb of the raid. He and the Colonel just had time to take cover under a heap of planks when the bomb exploded fifty yards away, on the rocky slope leading from the ramparts to the sea. Chunks and splinters of rock rained down upon the top of the planks.

" They must have seen me, after all," remarked the Colonel humorously, as the pair of them crawled out unscathed.

" It's an honour, sir," laughed the Adjutant. " They select you out of all Malta for their one bomb."

" More likely they're offended by the style of my pyjamas," said the Colonel.

Suddenly the Bofors which was installed at the Fort as protection against low-flying aircraft began firing rapidly. A Dornier, caught in the beam of a searchlight, was making frantic efforts to escape by flying low inland. It afforded the Pedro Bofors gunners an ideal target and they poured clip after clip at her. In a few moments they had shot the tail right off the machine. She turned with difficulty and flew heavily away in the direction of Valetta. The gunners were elated at their success. Their enthusiasm was somewhat diluted next morning. The stricken plane had dropped like a stone, with its full load of mines, doing more damage than if the gunners had left it alone.

Just before midnight the telephonist in the Command Post

received the " Raiders Passed " signal, and soon the sirens all over the island were announcing the " All Clear."

" Stand easy," the Gun Post Officer shouted to the gun crews.

" I think I'll get some sleep now," said the Colonel as he and the Adjutant moved away from the ramparts. " Though I've a strong idea it isn't over for the night."

" They've knocked off too soon for that, sir," agreed the Adjutant.

In the gun-pits the crews busied themselves checking up on equipment and replenishing ammunition. When this was accomplished to the satisfaction of the Nos. One they, too, were permitted to go to their dug-outs beside the guns to snatch a spell of sleep before the next bout.

The Colonel had his sleeping quarters in a building in the courtyard of the Fort. It was still dark when, turning over in his slumbers, he became half-consciously aware that the guns of the Fort were in action again. So used was he to the din that it called for no effort on his part to fall sound asleep again.

A loud swish, followed by a reverberating explosion, woke him a second time. In fact it nearly jerked him out of his bed. He jumped up, wide awake, and glanced at his watch. It was half-past four. Outside he could hear people running about and a certain amount of shouting. He thrust his feet into slippers, put on his tin-hat and a British Warm and hastened to see what had happened.

The night was still black and warm. A fierce raid was in progress. The searchlights were again busy weaving over the sky. The darkness was again lit by the red flashes of the bursting shells. But this time there were no flares. Bombs instead. And these were dropping all round with a deadly persistency.

Under the ramparts of the Fort, just where the road bent over the dry-moat into the Fort itself, was a row of four " cavaliers," large and lofty caverns hewn into the limestone by the old Knights of Malta and used by them for stabling and storage purposes. At present they were being utilised as sleeping quarters for some of the troops on the gun-site, principally Don R's, cooks, and spare gunners. Doors had been attached to the entrances, and other doors put in so that all the four " cavaliers " were inter-communicating.

It was hither the Colonel directed his steps, becoming conscious at the same time that the whole atmosphere was choked with fine dust. In the space outside the " cavaliers " the Battery Commander was slaving away in the darkness with a party of gunners trying to clear a way through a great pile of debris. He snatched a moment for a word with the Colonel.

" Bad mess, I'm afraid, sir," he said gravely.

A bomb had dropped on the ramparts, penetrated through eight feet of rubble and exploded in the centre of the chamber beneath.

" How many men inside ? " asked the Colonel.

" Can't say for certain, sir."

The " cavalier " had been completely demolished. It was now nothing more than a shapeless heap of rocks. Great blocks of limestone completely choked up the entrance. The gunners were trying to pull them away with drag-ropes.

" Together, heave ! . . . Together, heave ! . . ." the Major shouted in the darkness. On the ropes the men strained and grunted and tugged their hearts out in frantic efforts to release their comrades.

" Stop ! . . . Quiet, everybody . . ." ordered the Major every now and then.

And between the roar of the guns in the pits close by they would all listen attentively for any sign of life within.

From a naval barracks not far away some sailors had hurried over to help in the rescue work, and a Navy doctor was kneeling between two stretchers attending to a couple of gunners who had been injured by the blast while asleep in bed in the adjacent " cavalier."

" Together, heave ! . . ." the Major's voice rang out again. And the grim work went on once more.

The Battery sergeant-major had been dodging around making inquiries and checking up on names.

" I think I've got the lot, sir," he said, suddenly appearing out of the darkness at the Colonel's elbow.

" How many altogether ? "

" Six, sir. Five of ours, and another."

" What do you mean by that ? "

" Man from the other gun-site, sir. He had come over to spend his leave with his friend, Gunner Peach. He's inside there, too."

" Unlucky leave, poor devil," the Colonel commented with feeling.

" Lance-bombardier Rennie, fuse-setter on No. 4 gun, has hit it badly, too, sir."

" How ? "

" I'm told that when the whistle sounded he got up and went to his gun, but the No. One sent him back to bed again as he'd only just come off guard. . . . It's lucky the guns were in action, sir, or there'd have been another ten in that " cavalier."

" If the guns hadn't been in action it's quite possible there wouldn't have been any bombs falling, sergeant-major," the Colonel pointed out gently.

" Of course not, sir. I hadn't thought of that."

To the accompaniment of booming guns and exploding bombs, with the long white arms of the searchlights sweeping the dark sky above them, the group of gunners continued to haul and strain on their ropes. They had stripped themselves to the waist, and the sweat of their exertions wrought channels through the limestone dust that had settled thickly on their naked flesh. After a protracted spell of hauling, the Major, blear-eyed and hoarse from the dust in his throat, thought it was time to give the men a brief breather. But they refused to stop.

" Not till we get our pals out, sir," they shouted with one accord.

Gradually the weightiest limestone blocks were dragged from the entrance. Throughout the whole time there had been no sign of life from within. The rescuers were now able to man-handle the smaller debris, sorting from it with the aid of torches bits of bodies and scraps of clothing. These were placed on stretchers and conveyed to a shed adjoining the First Aid Post in the moat. There were no survivors. All six men had been blown to pieces. Eventually the rescue-party accounted for the lot. Except one head.

Afterwards, sick of the sight of ownerless arms and legs, the Major went off alone on a tour of inspection round the Fort. Among other things he discovered that the explosion had blown out all the windows of the Officers' Mess and of most of the buildings in the vicinity. There was hardly a door left intact and huge lumps of rock had been hurled into the rooms.

125

As he made his way to the Battery Office he heard the Gun Position Officer's megaphone bawling : " Cease Fire ! " The guns stopped. The raid was over. And the Major found himself appreciating, after the agitation of the night, the tranquillity that seemed to descend upon the Fort with the coming of dawn.

A quarter of an hour later the Battery sergeant-major entered the office.

" Have the men heard about the ' cavalier ' ? " the Battery Commander asked.

" Yes, sir. It has hit them up pretty badly."

" I was afraid so. . . . As soon as possible get as many as can be spared down to the football pitch and let them kick a ball about."

" Yes, sir."


## V—Von Oppenheim

As the year drew to a close a new problem thrust its attention on the garrison at Fort Pedro and, indeed, on all the other gun-sites on the island . . . the serious problem of sleep. The visits of the Luftwaffe became more and more frequent. more and more prolonged, more and more weighty. The guns seemed never to be out of action, day or night. Eight, even ten raids in twenty-four hours became a common occurrence. Also, there were the numerous " Air Observes " that never materialised into attacks. But the gunners had to " stand to " all the same. Sometimes one " Alert " alone would extend over a period of twelve hours, during which they never quitted the guns. It happened by night as well as by day. In addition immediately after each raid they had to buckle to and clean the guns ready for the next, an irksome, tedious job for weary men.

After weeks of such an existence the absence of a decent spell of unbroken sleep began to make itself felt. The gunners had to snatch what they could when they could. And this upset the routine of the Fort, especially in the matter of meals. As often as not the guns were in action at the usual meal-times. And when the men at last were free they were too tired-out to eat. They flung themselves on their bunks, tin-hats and all, and just passed out.

From this condition of affairs there arose two grievances. One minor, though irritating to the men, the other profound and engendering the bitterest of hate. The former was in the nature of a domestic grievance. . . .

Not even the best friend of the Gunners would ever seriously maintain the pre-eminence of the Royal Regiment in the matter of mounting guard. It is a pastime to which, for some reason or other the Gunners have never devoted themselves with the same enthusiasm as, say, the Brigade of Guards. With all their *esprit de corps*, it is fair to say that the Gunners are cheerfully willing to see the palm for smartness on guard carried off by the infantry, or any other department, every time. In any case, such were the sentiments prevailing among Don-Troop at Fort Pedro.

Suddenly, in the midst of the blitz, when sleep and rest were becoming a craving, the fiat went forth from the powers-that-be, that in future Gunner guards at Headquarters R.A. in Valetta were to be mounted on a much more spick-and-span standard than had hitherto been the custom. Things were to be quite ceremonial. The men were to be sized, rifle-drill and foot-drill was to be perfect, and boots polished till you could see your face in them. In addition the regimental band would play lively tunes in the Square at the changing of the guard.

Don-Troop did not approve. In fact they deeply resented the innovation. Their grouse was that gunners who were spending the best part of the day and night in action against enemy air-craft ought to be excused the pomp and panoply of peace-time soldiering.

" Who wants this Buckingham Palace stuff now ? " demanded Smiler irritably. " What's the point of it ? "

" I suppose it's done to keep up morale," the sergeant of No. 3 gun suggested.

" Hell ! . . . shouted Smiler. " Haven't we got Jerries enough to keep up our morale. I could understand if it only applied to field regiments. They haven't fired a round so far. I expect they are bored with nothing to do but fill-in shell holes. A bit of hot guard would be a nice change for them. But the Ack-Ack don't have time to get bored. Worse luck."

The grumbling continued. But the order remained. Don-Troop had to make the best of it. They combated the nuisance in the only way they could by having complete sets of highly polished boots, new and spotless' uniforms, and brand-new equipment kept specially in the Quartermaster's stores, only to be issued to each guard as it went on duty, and handed-in again the instant they returned to the Fort.

But Don-Troop's second grievance was, as already stated, a much more formidable affair. Not mere irritation but an undying hatred was implanted in every heart. It had become the obnoxious habit of the Germans, when they were not engaged in full-dress raids, to fill in the time with single-machine patrols. The practice in the daytime was for these planes to fly up and down the coast at a speed of 300 miles per hour, a distance of a couple of miles or so out, and at a height of O-feet. It was impossible for the light ack-ack to take them on. Occasionally the heavies put up a bit of shrapnel, but without much success. These planes would be relieved, and the same business went on for hours, with the gunners standing-to all the time.

The object of the patrol was to intercept British planes coming-in to land on the island, and reconnaissance planes going up. They had a certain measure of success. On one occasion the Fort Pedro garrison saw three Blenheims shot down in flames, one after the other. They lay blazing on the water together. An R.A.F. rescue launch which went out to pick up survivors was mercilessly machine-gunned by the enemy pilot. The launch drifted ashore on the little beach below the Fort. When the gunners waded out to it, they discovered that everyone on board was killed. The steersman had had his head blown off by a cannon-shell.

It was bad enough in the day-time. But it was the night patrol that got really under the skin of the gunners on Fort Pedro. Regularly every night at one a.m. along came a Ju. 88 and commenced to drone backwards and forwards along the coast for a stretch of five miles, always keeping a mile or two out, except for an occasional dash in to drop a bomb on Valetta. This went on till four in the morning. All chance of a few hours' rest was wrecked. The men turned out, stood-to in the gun-pits, listening for hour after hour to the heavy monotonous burr-r-r of the engine just out to sea, and returned to the dug-outs, sometimes without firing a round, weary and exasperated, just in time to be called out for the opening raid of the new day.

Night after night it was the same. It had been going on

for nearly a month. Each night at one a.m. the dug-outs on Fort Pedro echoed with curses.

Generally speaking the gunners' attitude towards individual enemy planes might be described as coldly impartial. They shot them down with no more personal feeling than is aroused by any one particular clay-pipe in a shooting-gallery. But now it was different. They grew to hate the night patrol with a murderous hate. They blasphemed it to the skies, and swore terrible vengeance on the pilot for their robbed sleep. Of course, it was not always the same identical plane. But the men preferred to consider that it was. In a moment of inspiration Smiler had christened it " Von Oppenheim," and the name stuck. Between " Von Oppenheim " and Fort Pedro existed the sort of enmity that is only to be cancelled out by death.

In the matter of individual hates among the gunners none surpassed in intensity that of the detachment commander of the Bofors gun on the Pedro site. The sergeant, a tall, thin, sandy-haired man, was of the type to whom excessive deprivation of sleep is disastrous. It upset his digestion, frayed his nerves, and reduced him in time to a condition of morose irritability. He became a changed man. And he never ceased informing his crew what he'd like to do to " Von Oppenheim " for changing him.

The detached commander enjoyed the luxury of a mattress, knocked together by the fitter from iron barbed-wire stakes, and finished off with wire-netting and empty sand-bags. It was nearly midnight. The Bofors crew had just come off the gun after a continuous " Alert " of six hours. Leaving a sentry and the telephonist in his dug-out near the gun to wake him if necessary, the sergeant flung himself down on his mattress and hoped for the best. It seemed he had hardly put his head on the pillow when he found the sentry shaking him.

" Oppy's here again."

The detachment commander let fly his usual oath.

" Up everybody," he shouted.

Grumbling and cursing the men flung on their boots and hurried back to the gun-pit.

In a little sand-bagged hut in the pit sat the telephonist. He was in touch with the Command Post and a message was just being relayed to him which had been received from Gun Operations Room.

" Take Post," shouted the sergeant to the crew.

" One plus . . . Two-seven-o degrees . . . Five miles S.E. of island . . . Course East . . . Height, 9,000 . . ." said the telephonist, repeating the message aloud.

The detachment commander waited at his elbow. After a minute or so came another message.

" This plot is now orbiting five miles south of the island . . ."

" Some bloody concert," the sergeant commented bitterly.

So regular were Von Oppy's movements that he knew it all off by heart.

" That means he's going to fly backwards and forwards for the rest of the night," he added.

He was quite right. The old game started, up and down the stretch of coast. When it came to Pedro's turn the 3.7's put up a shell or two. But Von Oppy didn't seem to mind.

The searchlights had adopted special tactics. They did not sweep the sky but followed the plane round with extinguished lights. Then, suddenly, one searchlight would shoot out a blinding beam in the direction of Von Oppy, hoping to strike lucky. If not the beam was instantaneously cut off, and the sky again became a pit of unbroken darkness. Occasionally Von Oppy seemed to be annoyed by these stabs, and opened up on the offending searchlight with its machine guns, the tracer bullets making little red-orange streaks down the white cone of light. Whereupon the searchlights Lewis gun retaliated. And the heavy guns would chime in with a few rounds.

So the game went on, as it had gone on every night for weeks. It was dull work for the Bofors. No use their opening up. Von Oppy never came within range. They simply had to wait. The weather was cold. It was raining heavily. After an hour the detachment commander, in the light of previous experience, decided to withdraw the gun crew, leaving a sentry on the gun, and the telephonist, to keep him informed of developments. The rest returned wet and cold to the dug-out, not to sleep, but to sit huddled round a little paraffin lamp made out of a cigarette tin, too browned off even to play cards.

Half an hour passed. The detachment commander sent a gunner over to relieve the telephonist. Outside Von Oppy could still be heard droning backwards and forwards high up in the sky. The persistent searchlight continued to prod for him. Now and again a few rounds went off from the Pedro's 3.7's.

Suddenly the newcomer at the telephone got a message from the Command Post.

"This plot has now changed course . . . Is in bearing Two-Seven-O degrees . . . Course, North-West."

The sentry ran to the dug-out.

"Oppy's coming in," he yelled.

The gun crew were on their feet in a moment, racing towards the gun. Overhead they could hear the drone of an engine, louder and louder. Yes, it certainly did seem they might have a chance at last.

"Take Post," shouted the detachment commander, almost cheerily.

They waited for five minutes . . . ten minutes . . .

"This plot changing course . . . Receding South-East," came the voice of the telephonist repeating aloud for the benefit of the detachment commander the message from the Command Post.

Cursing fantastically, and wet through again, the gun crew returned to the dug-out.

Half an hour later the telephonist received another message.

"This plot is losing height rapidly . . ."

Again the rush to the gun-pit. Again the wait in the darkness and pouring rain.

"This plot is now orbiting three miles South of island . . ."

Again the volley of curses, again the maddening sense of futility. Again the weary shuffle back to the dug-out.

And so it went on till half-past four when the "Raiders Passed" signal announced that Von Oppy, satisfied with having deprived them of another night's rest had departed to lay his own head on his pillow and sleep the sleep of the just. That reflection maddened them.

After this particular night the Colonel decided on measures to give the hard-pressed troops a break. It was arranged that two gun crews only should stand to on alternate nights when Von Oppy was amusing himself. If a raid developed, of course, the whole Troop came into action. It was also arranged that the Fort's Bofors should alternate with another Bofors stationed half-a-mile away.

On the first night these new measures were put into force the sandy-haired detachment commander spread himself out on his iron mattress to enjoy his first undisturbed sleep for a month. It was quite early, only half-past ten. Outside the dug-out the rain pelted down. Which increased the sergeant's satisfaction at the new routine. Heavy snores soon filled the dug-out.

Suddenly he was awakened by an excited sentry shaking his shoulder.

" Oppy's here, sergeant."

" You bloody fool ! " hissed the detachment commander viciously. " Don't you know it isn't our turn ? "

" He's coming right in," pursued the sentry. " I thought you wouldn't like to miss the chance, seeing how you feel about him."

The sergeant hesitated. It was not his night to turn-out. And sleep was sweet. On the other hand Oppy was sweeter. He could hear the heavy guns in action. Supposing there was a chance . . . The temptation was great.

He jumped off his mattress in pants and singlet, and flung on his overcoat.

" God help you if you've woke me for nothing," he threatened the sentry. " Come on . . . Up everybody ! . . ."

In the rain and darkness they stumbled across to the gun-pit. There was no doubt that Von Oppy seemed to be coming in, perhaps because of the poor visibility. They could hear the throb of the engine more clearly than ever before.

" Take Post ! " ordered the detachment commander.

He had hardly spoken when the black heavens were cleaved into two by the sudden beam of a searchlight. Another beam shot up. Tl e two raced towards each other and crossed low down on the sky. There, transfixed in the intersection, could be seen the silver shape of a plane.

" It's him ! . . . Oppy ! . . ." roared the detachment commander. " I'm having a go at him, out of turn or not."

Shells from the heavy guns were bursting round the plane in red flashes. All the Bofors guns within range streaked the black sky with their coloured tracers. Von Oppy continued to fly closer in. Unable to shake off the remorseless search-lights he appeared to have determined to try a bluff by coming over the island instead of turning back. His direction

was bringing him straight towards the Pedro Bofors gun-pit
from the sea.

" On ! . . . On ! . . ." shouted the layers, with the plane
in their sights.

The sergeant, with an effort, suppressed the order to fire
that was on his lips. He could afford to wait a bit with Oppy
coming straight towards them. He wanted to make certain
of the kill.

A few tremendous second passed. Oppy was now less
than fifteen hundred yards away, still unscathed.

" On ! . . . On ! . . ." again shouted the layers, keeping
the plane in their sights.

" Fire ! . . ." roared the sergeant.

The sergeant watched one . . . two . . . three . . . four
. . . five of his shells speed like red-hot cinders into the
fuselage of the plane. He saw a bright yellow flash in the
intersection of the white searchlights. Then a tiny tongue
of red flame that spread rapidly.

" Right in the guts ! . . ." he exclaimed joyfully. " Don't
waste another shell on him . . . Stand easy, boys ! "

They watched the plane losing height rapidly, still held in
the relentless searchlights. It dropped to two hundred feet,
one sheet of flame, that passed with a terrifying swish and
roar right over their heads, scattering white hot sparks and
bits of burning fuselage all over the gun-pit. The gunners
could feel the intense heat on their upturned faces. The
spectacle was so appalling that it moved even the sergeant
to a moment's pity. Then the enmity born of weeks of
shattered sleep re-asserted itself.

" Wonder how he liked his eggs fried," he grinned.

The flaming plane went on to crash on the little beach
below the ramparts of the Fort, amid the cheers of the entire
garrison, many of whom had run out in their night attire to
see the end of Von Oppy. They could even hear distant
cheers for Von Oppy's exit coming across the waters from
neighbouring gun-sites.

Early next morning, when the Bofors crew were doing
maintenance in the gun-pit, Smiler walked up in a mood of
suppressed excitement.

" Like to have a look, sergeant ? " he said.

The detachment gathered round while he unfolded a
pocket-handkerchief.

In the centre of the handkerchief lay a man's thumb, complete to the second joint.

" What is it ? " the sergeant asked.

" Oppy's thumb," said Smiler proudly. " He won't press any more buttons. I'm going to show it to the Colonel and ask him if I can keep it as a souvenir."

" Where did you get it ? "

" On the beach."

" Anything else there ? " inquired the sergeant, anxious himself for a souvenir of the night's great work.

" Nothing. Two dead blokes were chucked out of the plane and were hanging in the Dannert wire round the gun-site. No. 2 gun-pit has got a swastika off one of the wings. The only bit that wasn't burned-up."

The sergeant stared meditatively at the severed thumb.

" What'll you take for it ? " he asked, after a pause.

" Do you want it ? "

" I'd sooner have that thumb than the V.C.," said the sergeant, passionately.

" It's yours," replied Smiler, generously handing it over. " After all, you earned it. Not me."

" It'll look nice in a bottle with some methylated spirits," the sergeant mused aloud. " I'll keep it by the side of my bed. And whenever I get a touch of insomnia, I'll just look at it."


## VI—" No Friendly Aircraft Airborne "

THE telephonist in the Command Post at Fort Pedro wrote down the message coming over from Gun Operations Room and handed it to the Tactical Control Officer.

" No friendly aircraft airborne."

The T.C.O. was not surprised. Such messages were frequent nowadays, since the Luftwaffe had turned their attention to the aerodromes, spurred on by the arrival on the island of the first small contingent of Spitfires. Also the T.C.O. knew there was a special reason for the present message. At dusk, two days previous, nearly a hundred bombers had delivered a ferocious attack on one particular aerodrome. Next day two hundred planes in waves dive-bombed the same target.

Even now traces of the huge pall of smoke and dust that had ascended to a height of hundreds of feet still hung over the area.  The A.A. gunners upon whom the defence devolved entirely had had a bumper day, shooting down ten bombers and three Messerschmitts.  But the T.C.O. knew that we had had our losses too.

It was a morning mid-way in Spring, and by now the siege of Malta was well under way.  No one on the island cherished any doubts about that, least of all the A.A. gunners at Fort Pedro and the other sites.  Day by day since the commencement of the New Year the enemy air-raids had grown and grown in number and intensity.  In one month alone there had been two hundred and sixty-nine " Alerts."  And the total since Malta's advent into the front-line of battle, twenty-one months before, numbered over 2,000.  Sometimes the " Alerts " lasted for thirty-two hours without a break which meant the gunners standing-to all the time.  Gradually they were becoming worn down through lack of sleep.  At Fort Pedro Don-Troop looked back regretfully to the days when " Von Oppy " had kept them awake, as not being so bad after all.  Such sleep as they did manage to snatch was in the briefest of spells.  Three hours uninterrupted was a luxury.  Something to talk about.  Hardly had they fallen, dog-tired, into their bunks than the " Alert " whistles of the Command Post drove them remorselessly back to the guns.  To add to their discomforts it had been a cold, miserable winter, a phenomenon for Malta, with the *gregale* blowing from the north-west most of the time, and bringing with it incessant rains.

Everyone was aware of the big issues that were pending.  The Battle of Africa—which was Malta's battle, too—had again been joined.  Over in Libya, Rommel had once more taken the offensive and had driven the British back to Gazala whence, later on, he was to start his final rush towards Egypt and the Suez Canal, a push that was only to be brought to a standstill at El Alamein.  Malta, isolated in the Mediterranean, a lonely bastion of Empire, faced her new ordeal with undaunted courage.  It was no passive part she had to play.  Her job was to interfere as much as possible with the passage of reinforcements and supplies to Rommel, by sea as well as by air.  And the Luftwaffe paid her the tribute of recognising her importance by their deadly and

135

desperate attempts to neutralise her harbours and aerodromes.

So day and night the bombers hammered away, rarely letting-up for more than a few hours at a time.  In Valetta the death-roll mounted higher and higher.  And higher and higher mounted the spirit of the civilian population to meet its threatening destiny.

The tactics of the Luftwaffe were nearly always the same. First would arrive swarms of Me. 109 and Me. 110 fighters clearing the air for a wave of Ju. 88 bombers.  After these had unloaded their cargoes all the planes departed.  Immediately there followed another wave of Messerschmitts which ironed out the way for the Ju. 87's who came in last of all and dive-bombed their targets with the utmost ferocity.

Against these overwhelming attacks the handful of Spitfires and Hurricanes fought desperately and without rest.  Often they went up with odds more than fifteen to one against them.  Though they never failed to exact their toll, their numbers were not sufficient to prevent the raids materialising. Besides which, the Hurricanes were outclassed in speed by the new Me. 109's and Ju. 88's and Ju. 87's, much better types than had taken part in the Battle of Britain.  Also, the aerodromes received such a pounding from the dive-bombers that they frequently became unserviceable for a while. Planes were destroyed on the ground, and as fast as bomb-holes in the run-ways were filled-in new ones appeared.  On such occasions it was that the gun-sites received the significant message : " No friendly aircraft airborne."  Then the A.A. gunners knew that for the time being the defence of the island and all the graver issues this implied, depended upon them alone.

On this particular morning three raids had materialised and it was not till half-past two in the afternoon that the cooks at Fort Pedro had a chance of bringing up dinner to the hard-pressed crews in the gun-pits.  The men took it in turns to eat, while at the same time cleaning the guns and replenishing the half-empty ammunition racks from the dwindling stores in the tunnel in the dry moat.  Up and down the steep flight of stone steps the ammunition numbers trudged in pairs, each carrying a box containing a couple of shells between them.

Suddenly, in the middle of this snatched meal, the Command Post whistles sounded another " Alert."  Cursing vigorously the men dumped their food into what they hoped would be safe spots and dashed once more to their gun stations.

In the Command Post the " plot " for the raid was coming in from Gun Operations Room. Drawing and measuring on the white talc surface of his plotting board as the information reached him, the Tactical Control Officer began to knit his eyebrows.

" Wherever they're going, they'll be passing right overhead of us," he shouted to the Gun Position Officer, standing beside the spotter who was raking the sky through the Telescope Identification for a first sight of the raiders.

" Plane ! . . ." yelled the spotter almost at the same moment. " Three of them, sir," he added to the G.P.O. " Ju. 87's . . . Flying backside foremost, sir. What does that mean ? "

He broke off and shouted the bearing and angle of sight to the predictor and height-finder crews to enable them to get on to the target. Staring through his glasses the G.P.O. could now see what had struck the spotter as odd about the raiders. Instead of flying in the usual V-formation, two were in front and one behind, like a V flying backwards. The G.P.O. hadn't much time to give to speculations on the meaning of this novelty. He was more concerned with the fact that, as the T.C.O. had predicted, the planes were coming in from the sea directly over the gun-site. They were about 12,000 feet up.

" Height-finder on target . . . Predictor on target . . ." announced the Numbers One.

Before they could continue the usual routine the voice of the Tactical Control Officer bawled from the Command Post a new order that had just come through from Gun Operations Room.

The G.P.O.'s megaphone instantly roared, and the guns, without further need of instructions, were rapidly swung to a pre-determined bearing and height. Each of them quickly got into action and their shells burst in the pathway of the in-coming planes along with those from other gun-sites that had now opened fire.

The G.P.O. watching through his glasses, was thinking they were making it uncomfortably hot for the raiders when he suddenly saw the left-hand plane peel off from the

formation and start to dive straight at the gun position. For
half-a-second he stared, fascinated by the menace of it.
The unearthly scream of the Stuka grew shriller and shriller
as it plummetted upon them.

" Gun Control ! . . . " he roared, so as to leave the guns
free in this emergency to fire on their own initiative with
their special low fuse.

In the gun-pits the layers turned their handles frantically
traversing and depressing the guns as rapidly as they could
to keep the descending bomber in their sights. The loaders
rammed the shells home at a speed beyond all their previous
best efforts. Not a man in the pits but realised fully that
his fate was bound up in the matter of the next few seconds.
They had now only themselves to look to for salvation. In
between the roar of their shells sounded the pom-pom-pom-
pom of the Bofors guns on the Fort a short distance away,
and the rattle of their own Bren-gun. But above all the
din, splitting it with a shriek that grew more terrifying as
it came nearer and nearer, the noise of the diving plane
continued to pierce their ears.

By now it had dropped down to a thousand feet. The G.P.O.,
head bent right back, saw three bombs shoot away from it,
falling, so it appeared, straight on top of him. The dive had
finished. For a fateful second or two the plane seemed to
hover before commencing its climb back. Now came a
great burst of fire from every gun on the site, 3.7's, Bofors
and Bren, all anxious to take advantage of this weakest
moment in a dive-bomber's career, and to shoot it in the
belly. Simultaneously with the roar of the guns sounded
the terrific explosion of the bursting bombs, accompanied
by a big flash which enveloped No. 2 gun-pit in flames.

The G.P.O. was hurled bodily against the sand-bag wall
of the predictor pit. When he recovered breath he heard
groans proceeding from within.

" Man hurt . . . Stretcher . . ." someone was calling.

On running into the pit he discovered the No. 4 twisted
on the ground in agony. A bomb splinter had smashed his
leg below the knee. Two of his comrades were slitting the
leg of his trousers with a knife so as to apply a field dressing.
It was a large wound and they had to use three of the ordinary
pads to cover it. The G.P.O. took out a cigarette, lit it and
placed it between the wounded man's lips.

" Thanks, sir," the sufferer managed to gasp out.  " Didn't know there were any left on the island."

" You'll be all right," the G.P.O. comforted him.

The bombs were no longer falling.  It had all been a matter of seconds.  Away in the distance could be heard the drone of the departing bombers, on their way to their main target. The guns still fired spasmodically, though by now the planes were out of range.

Hurrying out of the predictor pit the G.P.O. was horrified to see, for the first time, that No. 2 gun-pit was in flames. He was even more horrified when one of the crew, the skin all burned off his face, staggered from the interior, through the dust and smoke, and collapsed outside.

" Stand easy !  . . ." he roared through his megaphone to the other pits.  " Come on, everybody  . . . Give a hand to No. 2 pit  . . . Jump to it  . . ."

The spasmodic gun-fire ceased as the men tumbled out of the pits and rushed across to No. 2.  The first man to arrive at the entrance looked inside, stopped dead, swung round, and was violently sick.

Hearing a voice at his side the G.P.O. turned to confront the Colonel.

" What has happened, Bruce ? "

" I'm just going over to see, sir," replied the G.P.O. " Direct hit, I'm afraid."

Together they strode across to the pit.  Inside, the camouflage netting was burning.  The gunners from the other pits were already tearing it down and stamping on it to put out the flames.  The covers of the sand-bags were alight.  In the racks all round the pit the ammunition had caught fire, filling the place with violent flashes and disconcerting " whoofs " as the charges blew up.  Strewn about the ground lay the gun crew, seven of them dead and one dying in silence.  One of the ammunition numbers was in a sitting position, still holding the bottom half of the shell he had been carrying to the loading tray when the bomb fell. The top half was embedded in his stomach.  The fuse-setter had had the front of his face sliced off by a bomb-splinter which had caught him under the chin and cut upwards. The rest of the crew betrayed no visible sign of injury.  But they all bore upon them a mark which the onlookers found more dreadful and chilling to behold than the gaping wounds

139

of their comrades. Each of their faces was distorted by the same faint smile. But not a smile of peace. It was an empty, vacuous smile, eloquent only of the quenched intelligence behind it.

The dying man lay at the entrance to the pit. He, also, showed no trace of injury except for the dribble of blood trickling from the side of his mouth. He remained silent and motionless, his face a waxy pallor, and his wide-open eyes glazed. From one of the torn sand-bags a tiny rivulet of sand was pouring down the back of his neck.

The Colonel hurried back to the Command Post.

" Report to G.O.R. that we've had a direct hit on No. 2 pit, and the gun is out of action," he said to the telephonist. " And tell them to hurry along an ambulance."

Meanwhile stretcher-bearers from the First-Aid Post in the moat had arrived, and substituted a large shell-dressing for the makeshift field dressings on the leg of the wounded man in the predictor pit. The No. 2 of the height-finder crew was also a casualty. A piece of splinter had hit him in the back and emerged at the chest. He was unconscious, and moaning in pain. The first-aid party did what they could to ease him.

By now the flames in the gun-pit had been extinguished and the ammunition removed to a place of safety. Having done everything that could be done men clustered outside in a gloomy silence, depressed by the tragic fate of their comrades. Fort Pedro had had bad knocks before, but this dwarfed them all. A complete gun-crew wiped out in a matter of seconds. The men they had known and lived with for so many years, sharing their pleasures and hardships in all parts of the world, now lay merely bleeding and grinning corpses. . . .

Inside the gun-pit, stinking of bomb-fumes and with blood soaking into the dust and sand, the Gun Position Officer was silently praying that the ambulance would soon arrive so that they could rid themselves of the gruesome spectacle. He was joined by the Battery Commander who, in order to tear his mind from those terrible smiling faces, began an examination of the gun itself. A bomb had hit the barrel just above the recuperator and had scraped off a piece of steel. All the glass on the dials had been shattered. But apart from this the gun appeared to be completely undamaged.

" A testimony to British workmanship," commented the Battery Commander.

But the G.P.O. at that moment was beyond the power of anything to distract his mind from the horror that had descended on it

The Battery Commander walked out of the gun-pit and past the group of silent gunners. His eye happened to alight on one man, standing slightly apart. It was Doughy, with the dirt and sweat of his rescue work begriming his face.

Still under the necessity of finding something to think about beyond those terrible faces in the gun-pit, if only for a moment, the Battery Commander suddenly beckoned Doughy towards him.

" How are you getting on with your transfer to R.C. ? " he asked.

He already knew that, much to his surprise, Doughy had managed to produce the necessary evidence that his motives for wishing to become a convert were sincere, and had started his preparation.

" I've changed my mind, sir," replied Doughy.

" Not getting married after all, eh ? "

" I mean, sir, changed my mind about becoming R.C."

The Major asked no more questions about that. He wasn't particularly interested in the ebb and flow of Doughy's religious convictions.

" What about the girl ? " he asked.

" We're hoping to get married soon, sir."

The Major shrugged his shoulders and strode on.

At last the ambulance arrived. An R.A.M.C. orderly entered the pit, took a hypodermic syringe from its webbing case, and injected a dose of morphia into the forearm of the wounded man. Having satisfied himself that all the others were dead he proceeded to the predictor pit and administered morphia to the other wounded there. Stretcher-bearers carried them to the ambulance.

A little later on, the Battery Sergeant-Major sat in his office with a small pile of luggage labels on the table. Upon each of them he inscribed the name of a dead man, his number, regiment, the words " Killed in Action," the place and the date. Having finished he gathered up the handful of labels and hurried over to No. 2 gun-pit, where eight bodies lay stretched in a row side by side on blankets. One by one he called out the names, and one by one the blankets were wrapped round the dead men and the identification labels attached. The gunners bore them to the Matador lorry that waited outside the Fort to convey them to the mortuary in Valetta. When the final load had departed the G.P.O. drew a deep breath of thankfulness and, avoiding a last look round, almost fled from the empty gun-pit. Feeling a great craving for living companionship he made his way to the Battery Office.

" All finished ? " said the Battery Commander.

" Yes, thank God," replied the G.P.O., wearily.

He sank into a chair, not wishing to talk but just to sit here for a bit in silence. On the B.C.'s table stood eight little heaps, the personal belongings of the dead men, which had been collected from their pockets and handed in by the sergeant-major. Uppermost on each heap was the man's A.B. 64, his pay-book. The G.P.O. idly picked up the nearest and glanced at the name. It happened to be the sergeant of the ill-fated gun.

Mechanically he commenced turning over the leaves. He came to the soldier's will form that is such an essential part in every A.B. 64. His eye was arrested by the bald statement :

" All to my wife."

The G.P.O. recalled that the sergeant had a Maltese wife who was at present living in England.

He closed the A.B. 64 and replaced it on its heap.

There was a rap at the door and the Battery Sergeant-major entered.

" The Ten Brigadiers have just arrived, sir," he announced.

" Ha, ha ! . . . That's superb," laughed the G.P.O., with bitter irony. " Tell them to push off. We don't fancy them to-day."

The B.S.M. remained in the doorway with immobile face, watching the Battery Commander.

" The Ten Brigadiers " was a concert-party, formed of ack-ack N.C.O.'s and gunners, which toured the gun-sites and hospitals giving shows. Their motto was : " The Show goes on," whether raids were on or not. Successors to " The Whizz-Bangs " of the peaceful months before the first arrival of the Luftwaffe, they possessed some excellent talent and were extremely popular among the troops. After a humble beginning in khaki they had blossomed out into white tuxedos. The Sappers built them a portable stage with lighting which they carried about with them. Their greatest triumph was a " command performance " at the British Institute in Valetta before all the dignitaries of the island. It proved such a success that they had to give a repeat.

The Battery Commander looked thoughtful.

" What do you think yourself, sergeant-major ? " he asked.

" The men have been looking forward to the show very much, sir."

" We mustn't act too hastily," the Major observed, sympathetically to the G.P.O., after a pause. " I know what's in your mind. It's in mine, too. But we've got to think of the living as well as the dead. We shall certainly bitterly disappoint a good many of the troops if we send the Brigadiers away now. God knows when they'll get another chance of seeing the show. And God also knows they deserve all the relaxation that comes their way. This isn't peace-time. Things that in the usual run of events would shock susceptibilities don't possess the same significance now. I know it sounds crude. But these are crude days. I mustn't overlook the fact, either, that this show to-night is a bit of a blessing. It may help to divert the men's minds from the disaster. Those who really consider it disrespectful—close friends of the casualties and so on—are always at liberty to stay away."

He turned to the sergeant-major. " Let them carry on. Show them where to put up their sticks."

" I think I've done the right thing," he said to the Gun Position Officer when the sergeant-major had departed.

" I know you have, sir," replied the G.P.O. sincerely. " I was being an old-fashioned clown . . . You know, sir, the damn funny thing to me is I'm certain I shall come along to the show with the rest of you this evening, and sit in the front row enjoying myself."

## VII—Barrage in Full Blast

" CAN you see Father Joseph of the Church of the Immaculate Conception, sir ? " said the Adjutant one afternoon, opening the door of the Colonel's office at regimental H.Q.

"Never heard of him," replied the C.O. "What does he want?"

"He is being reticent, sir. Says he has come out from Valetta especially to see you on a matter of importance."

"All right. Let him come in."

A big, burly Maltese priest entered wearing a black over-coat over his soutane, which was knotted at the waist by a white silken cord. His broad, fleshy face and heavy jowl at once reminded the Colonel forcibly of Mussolini. The thought crossed the Colonel's mind that such a brawny fellow would have looked more at home in a soldier's uniform than in a priest's cassock.

"Sit down, Father Joseph," he said. "What is it you want to see me about?"

"Forgive me for disturbing you, Colonel," began the priest in a booming voice. "I have called upon a matter of some consequence to a parishioner of mine. A young girl named Carmela Camilleri. She is about to marry a soldier in your regiment who, I understand, is stationed in the Fort. I have been asked to put up the banns, and before doing so, for the protection of the girl, I wish to make a few enquiries."

The Colonel nodded slowly.

"What is the man's name, Father?"

"Henry Baker. He is a gunner."

"Ah, I remember something about this," said the Colonel. "So he is determined to marry the girl after all."

He paused for a moment or two and continued:

"I'll make no bones about it with you, Father. I, personally, feel strongly on the subject of mixed marriages. But, of course, I can do nothing officially to stop it. The man is free to marry whom he chooses. But I confess, I don't like it."

It was the priest's turn to nod and he did so emphatically.

"Your feelings are mine, Colonel," he boomed. "I consider it most undesirable for any of my parishioners to marry outside the faith. But I also have to consider that if they do not get married worse may happen. All I can do is to assure myself that the young man is worthy. I have to protect my parishioner, however misguided she may be."

The Colonel was thinking that, of the pair, it was probably Gunner Henry Baker who stood most in need of protection.

" Did the girl ask you to see me ? " he asked, with a faint smile.

" No. She loves. Therefore she trusts. I have come on my own initiative."

" Very well, Father Joseph. I'll do all I can for you. What is it you want to know ? "

" I want to know whether there is anything about this young man that makes him undesirable as a husband. Apart, of course, from his faith. Is he really single ? Is he a man of good character ? The girl is a good girl and I do not want any harm to befall her."

" If you don't mind waiting a minute, I'll send for his documents," said the Colonel.

While they were waiting the Command Post whistle sounded a new " Alert." Suddenly the Colonel's office shook with a big concussion. The priest, involuntarily, half-rose from his chair.

" No need to be alarmed, Father," said the Colonel. " It is only our own guns firing. You haven't been on a gun-site in action before ? It's inclined to be noisy."

In a little while the roar of the Pedro guns was almost drowned in the general din outside. Grand Harbour Barrage was in full blast, and such a blast as rendered its efforts of a year previous puny by comparison. The whole island trembled under the colossal shock and the heavens above rolled and roared in one vast, undying thunder-clap. Now and then they could hear the deep explosion of bursting bombs.

" They're after the *Penelope* again," said the Colonel, half to himself. " I hope to God she comes through all right."

Father Joseph moved his lips in a word or two of silent prayer and crossed himself.

After a few minutes the Adjutant entered and placed before the Colonel a sheaf of papers among which were Doughy's A.B. 64 (his pay book), his attestation papers on which were entered details of birth, age, etc., and his crime sheet. Together with Father Joseph, amid the tornado of Grand Harbour Barrage outside, the Colonel began to examine the documents. The A.B. 64 showed that Doughy was not already paying any marriage or maintenance allowance, and the attestation form indicated that he was a single man and had no children.

K                           145

" I think that should go a long way to satisfy you, Father,"
said the Colonel. " Of course, we can't guarantee that he
isn't married. A man can lie on his attestation. But I've no
reason to suppose this is the case with Baker."

They turned to the crime sheet. The priest pounced on
the entry of Doughy's fourteen days' detention, and began
to question the Colonel closely on Doughy's character.

" I shouldn't pay much attention to that," said the Colonel.
" It was a bit of a mystery to me at the time. But I've since
heard that the man was suffering from the shock of having
his best friend killed. I think I can assure you about his
character. He is a steady, sober, conscientious fellow. A
good soldier."

The brawny priest, looking more like Mussolini than ever,
sat back in his chair with the air of a man who has performed
his duty.

" I hope that has satisfied you," continued the Colonel.
" I will embody the information in an official letter which
I will have despatched to you at once."

The raid on Grand Harbour having ended, the priest took
his departure. Later in the afternoon the Colonel wrote on
a sheet of notepaper embossed with the Royal Arms :

" Dear Father Joseph : With reference to your call upon
me to-day, having examined the papers of Gunner Henry
Baker of the 777th H.A.A. Regiment, I beg to inform you
that, to the best of my belief and knowledge, he is a single
man and that he is of good character."

He picked up the regimental rubber stamp, dabbed it at
the foot of the letter and wrote his signature across.

" Put this in an envelope and have it sent off at once to
Father Joseph," he said to the Adjutant.

In the Mess that evening he mentioned Father Joseph's
visit briefly to the Battery Commander.

" So that's that," said the B.C. " Stupid fellow."

Nothing more was said on the subject or on the Colonel's
pet obsession, mixed marriages. The conversation centred
round the afternoon's dive-bombing attack on the cruiser
*Penelope* in Grand Harbour. For days now the *Penelope* while
undergoing repairs in the dockyard had been subject to
incessant and ferocious attacks by the Luftwaffe. It was the

*Illustrious'* business all over again, but much more fierce. Again as in the *Illustrious'* days the question on everybody's lips was whether the ship would be sunk before she could be repaired and slip out into the open sea again. For days the battle had gone on and the *Penelope*, quite apart from the help of Grand Harbour Barrage, had ,put up a magnificent fight with her own guns against the swarms of dive-bombers that descended on her. It was a fight against terrific odds that kindled the enthusiasm and pride of the entire population. But it was also a fight against time, and trepidations were mingled with hopes. Meanwhile dockyard workers, sailors, and soldiers laboured heroically day and night to complete the repairs.

" Does anyone know what happened to *Penelope* this afternoon ? " asked the Colonel.

" Pity this isn't one of Peter's nights, sir," said the Gun Position Officer. " Then we could be sure of the latest dope."

" I may be able to tell you a little, sir," chimed in a young subaltern from a 25-pounder battery who was the guest of the Tactical Control Officer. " It isn't much. But coming along here this evening I dropped into the Union Club for a moment."

" Guessing we'd gone dry," laughed the G.P.O. " Sage lad."

" I heard them saying at the Union Club, sir," continued the subaltern, " that the Gunnery Officer has been killed and the Captain wounded."

" That's bad news. What about the ship herself ? "

" Untouched, sir. Though the Stukas dived through the barrage lower than ever. Doesn't she have marvellous luck, sir ? "

" I only hope it will continue a bit longer," said the Colonel.

" There was also a bit of gossip going at the Club, sir, on the prospects of an invasion."

" That gossip has been going on ever since the blitz intensified," said the Battery Commander. " I'm not surprised either. From the way the Luftwaffe seem all out to smash up everything, one can imagine anything happening."

" Do you think there's any possibility of an invasion, sir ? " the subaltern asked the Colonel.

" All I can say is that I'm told our air reconnaissance reports no signs of the massing of troop-carrying vessels or landing craft in Sicily or at Reggio."

" They may try to put another Crete over on us," observed the Gun Position Officer.

" I don't think so," said the Colonel firmly. " Malta's a very different proposition from Crete. Besides, we've learned our lesson. I know that very complete preparations have been made for all contingencies. You've got your invasion task like all the rest of us, I suppose ? " he added, addressing the 25-pounder subaltern.

" Yes. We're all ready. Hoping it will come, sir. So far this has been a most unfriendly war to us. We haven't been able to get a shot in edgeways. Not even when the *Radnor* was sunk," complained the subaltern.

" Perhaps I'm being dense, but I don't follow," said the Gun Position Officer. " What's the *Radnor* got to do with it ? "

" Well, you remember that when the *Radnor* came in she didn't dock in the Harbour," began the subaltern. " They took her round to Kalifrana Bay to be unloaded. As a protection against air-raids the surrounding gun-sites sent along heavy guns and Bofors which were mounted during the night on the cliffs round the bay."

" Yes. Our site over the other side of Valetta supplied a 4.5 and a Bofors," the Colonel mentioned.

" My battery got orders to send along a Troop of 25-pounders in case of an E-boat attack," the subaltern continued. " We camouflaged in caves on the beach along with some 18-pounders. As you know, sir, the dive-bombers came along in due course. A hundred of them, with an escort of Me. 109's. The ship got a bad knock. I saw jets of steam coming from the decks and oil began to flood the sea. She listed heavily over to the side. Unloading had stopped, of course, and all the crew were taken off.

" After the bombers had gone our Adjutant came racing up on a motor-cycle and told the Troop-Commander that R.H.Q. had just received orders to sink her by gun-fire. I suppose she was more useful to us under the water than blown-up in another raid. The Adjutant said he was sending us down some armour-piercing to do the job. The A.P. arrived in due course. We loaded, and the Troop Commander was just waiting for the signal to fire when, hang it, if the ship didn't quietly heel over and sink before our eyes. So we didn't get even the satisfaction of doing that job."

" Some of you young fellows are going to be busier soon,"

said the Colonel. " I understand arrangements are being made for officers from field regiments to be seconded to gun-sites, to fill up casualties among personnel. The heavies have been suffering badly in the past few weeks and can do with a bit of assistance. We're all beginning to feel slightly worn down."

" We'll all be jolly glad of a chance to do something, sir," said the subaltern. " Though I don't suppose we'll be much good at first. It's rather a change for us."

The Colonel checked a smile. He guessed that the thought in the subaltern's mind would have been more accurately expressed by the words : " It's a bit of a come-down for us." The Colonel knew all there was to be known about the sense of pride among field gunners and their attitude of lofty superiority towards other branches.

" Don't worry. You'll pick it up quickly. We were a field regiment ourselves when war broke out," he contented himself with saying.

## VIII—Under Siege

THE rigours of the siege hardened. In addition to the incessant bombing both garrison and civilians alike were facing the serious food shortage due to the difficulty of forcing convoys through to the island under a sky thick with enemy aircraft. Two breadless days a week was now the regulation at Fort Pedro. The gunners had to put up with issue biscuits instead. Lentils took the place of potatoes. Lentils and bully beef, or M. and V. (tinned stew) day after day. Worse still, the Naffy canteen had run dry. Not a Blue Label had been seen for weeks. At the Fort the gloomy impression prevailed that there wasn't a single bottle of beer left on the entire island. Against this, the fact that practically the whole of Malta was milk-less, except for the dried variety, seemed to the troops merely a minor disaster. Much more serious was the famine in cigarettes. They were now rationed to twenty-five a week, which number, by carefully hoarding fag-ends and re-rolling them, they managed to increase to twenty-seven.

No relief from these privations was to be found in Valetta. The population was as badly off as the troops. Restaurants and cafés were closed down. Most of the civilians were doing without even tea or coffee. They had to depend on Victory kitchens for getting a meal. A hundred thousand meals were served a day. And that wasn't enough. Such troops as went into the town for their twenty-four hours' leave found it almost impossible to buy anything to eat. So they were provided with food chits for Command Fair, a large hall, formerly a police headquarters, which was equipped by the military authorities for the purpose of supplying meals exclusively to troops.

One result of the present discomforts of Valetta was a sudden return to popularity of the military rest camp in the north of the island. Hitherto the Fort Pedro gunners on their eagerly awaited five days' leave (which happened once in three months) had preferred spending it among the bustle and bars and cinemas of the capital rather than at the rest camp, where there was not much else to do but bathe. But now you could get food, regular if not in large quantities, at the camp. And that made a difference.

In truth, there was little inducement nowadays to spend a leave in Valetta. The city had become a ruinous ghost. Most of the popular haunts in the Strada Stretta had put up their shutters. Many bars were out of action. Some of the cinemas had been destroyed. Many of the streets were so choked with ruins as to be impassable, especially the narrow, old, " staircase " streets in the neighbourhood of the Cathedral of St. John, which itself had been badly damaged. In the square courtyard facing what had once been the Royal Library all that survived was the statue of Queen Victoria surveying with Jubilee placidity, the desolation on either side of her. The Governor's Palace had received a direct hit which demolished the magnificent staircase, and the great banqueting hall where the Grand Masters of the past had feasted and revelled. In the Strada Reale piles of broken masonry were all that remained of the handsome portico of the Opera House. Of the Law Courts the skeleton of one archway alone still stood. Two of the famous ornate Auberges of the Knights of Malta, the Auberge d'Auvergne and the Auberge de Bavarie, were mere heaps of ruins. Churches had been shattered and houses and buildings destroyed in their thousands. This was especially the case in the Three Cities—Senglea, Cospicua and Vittorioso —the neighbourhood surrounding the Naval Dockyard. So badly had the district suffered that scores of streets were blocked with the ruins of houses, and there was hardly an unshattered window to be found anywhere.

The great bulk of all this devastation had been concentrated in the three months or so since the siege began in earnest. Within the same three months the casualties among the civilian population had more than doubled the total reached during the whole eighteen months' bombing from Mussolini's declaration of war in June 1940 till December 1941. Valetta, in fact, now wore the battle-scarred visage of the veteran, and the change was reflected in the mood of the Maltese themselves. Much of their volatility and lightheartedness had disappeared under pressure of circumstances. It gave place to an intense bitterness against their enemies, especially the Italians, and a grim determination to see the thing through at whatever the cost. It was a spirit that helped them to face cheerfully the additional hardship of one of the wettest winters on record, no small trial to a sun-loving population forced to spend the bigger part of its days and nights in damp air-raid shelters.

Like Valetta, Fort Pedro bore its own visible scars of the never-ceasing battle. The gun positions were ringed round with bomb craters, testifying to the accuracy of the work of the Stukas which were now beginning to concentrate on gun-sites. Bomb-splinters had heavily pockmarked the bastion walls. Regimental H.Q. had been destroyed and was now operating from a house in the Melita Road. A little unused chapel near the Officers' Mess lay in ruins. The Mess itself was half-wrecked. The sleeping-quarters of the Battery and Regimental staffs was so badly damaged that the men were transferred to the Naffy building. Three more of the "cavaliers" had been demolished by a direct hit.

In personnel Don-Troop at the Fort had suffered severely. The disaster at No. 2 gun-pit brought their total casualties to twenty men killed and ten wounded, getting on for a quarter of their strength. At the regiment's other sites the position was almost as bad, and three officers had been killed and two wounded. Few sites on the island, indeed, had escaped damage and casualties since the Stukas had turned attention to them. The gunners could feel the pressure upon the ground defence becoming heavier every day. Their burdens increased as the attacks worked up to a crescendo and the aerodromes were rendered more and more unserviceable. For long spells they alone became responsible for the defence of the island. They slaved at the guns, night and day, without relief. The night raids they found especially nerve-racking because, in the darkness, amid all the racket of the firing, they could neither see nor hear the bombs as they fell from the Stukas. They never knew, from second to second, when the bombs might start bouncing upon the gun-site. All they could hear was the scream of the diving planes overhead. Which was no comfort at all!

In the half-empty ammunition racks round the gun-pits the gunners could read, if they required any further enlightenment, the critical nature of those fateful days. Not only had food become short, but also ammunition. Supplies had to be carefully conserved for no one could be sure, when or whether, the next convoy would get through. Instead of being able, as in the days of the attack on the *Illustrious,* to fire *ad lib.* at the rate of a hundred shells a minute the Bofors were now rationed to fifteen rounds per gun per day. At the Fort Pedro site the heavy guns were limited to a daily allowance of forty-three rounds, roughly ten rounds a gun. This at a time when the attack from the air was reaching the limit in ferocity, and it could be accounted a comparatively quiet day if only six raids developed. This enforced economy meant cutting out all chance shooting. Ammunition had to be strictly preserved for big raids or for actual attacks on the gun-sites themselves. Even then it was a perilously small allowance. And the knowledge that they had not a round to spare when firing threw an extra strain on the gunners.

It was 8 p.m. A warm night for a change, and faintly lit by the rising moon. A fortnight had elapsed since No. 2 gun-pit at Fort Pedro received the direct hit. The pit was now in action again. The damaged 3.7 had been repaired in the R.A.O.C. workshops near Valetta, and towed back to the site by a Scammel lorry. A new gun-crew had been compiled from spare numbers in the other three pits. This, of course, meant still harder work for everybody. Leave was cut to the minimum and chances of getting a stand-in became practically negligible.

It had been a day of attacks and an " Alert " was on at the moment. In the Command Post the Tactical Control Officer was having a very busy evening indeed with ten single " plots " on his board at the same time. A mixed flock of ten Ju. 88's and three-engined Savoias, approaching from the north of the island, had split up and were coming in from various directions. So the T.C.O. had the job of keeping track of ten planes, each on a different bearing that was itself continually altering. In the darkness the guns, with the help of radio-location, occasionally sent off a round or two. But the firing was perforce desultory because the raiders persisted in flying in and out again without any apparent method. Now and then the deep boom of an exploding bomb echoed across the harbour from Valetta.

From time to time the T.C.O., with his squared map of Malta divided into smaller squares, received word from Gun Operations Room to box-barrage a plane that was coming in.

This gave him the particular bit of square to fire on and the height. Having got the bearing, the range and angle of sight he passed them to the Gun Position Officer and the guns opened up. As soon as they did so, as often as not, a plane would appear for a moment in the beam of a searchlight.

Suddenly, without warning a bomb burst about three hundred yards away, just outside the Fort. A second later the crew in the predictor pit became aware of a loud swish coming towards them accompanied by a terrific draught. Standing near to the pit the G.P.O. heard a faint cry within, followed by the sound of a scuffle. Next instant he was astounded to see the predictor crew rushing pell-mell from the pit.

" What the hell's up ? . . . Get back, damn you all . . ." he yelled.

Nobody took any notice. He ran into the predictor pit to discover the reason for the sudden panic. An amazing sight confronted him, a sight that made his own heart jump a couple of beats. The swish and draught had been caused by a 750-lb. bomb that had fallen just within the sand-bagged wall of the predictor pit and buried its nose deeply into the ground. There, threatening at any moment to explode and blow the pit to pieces, it stuck up vertically like some monstrous, rusty-coloured, vegetable growth. But what froze the G.P.O. was the glimpse he obtained of the terror-stricken face of the No. 3 of the predictor crew. In falling the bomb had pinned the man's left foot between it and the wall of the pit, and he was struggling frantically to extricate himself. The top of the

bomb reached almost to his hip.  He pushed, pulled, and
clawed at it in his desperate efforts to loosen the grip.  His eyes
bulged with horror.  Perspiration streamed down his face.
Uncanny noises, half-gasps, half-moans, issued from his dry
throat.

The G.P.O. dashed forward to help the unfortunate man.
Just as he did so the latter, by a supreme effort, managed to
shift the sand at the base of the bomb sufficiently to enable
him to wrench his foot free.  Frenzied by his ordeal, and
barely conscious of what he was doing, he thrust the G.P.O.
violently aside with both hands and fled from the pit.

It was time now to attend to the safety of the others, the
height-finder crew and the Command Post Staff.

" Get out, everybody ! . . ." the G.P.O. roared through his
megaphone.  " Quick ! . . . Get under cover . . . Move ! . . ."

With the predictor pit temporarily out of action the guns were
not getting orders and had stopped firing.  This did not matter
so much as it might have because the raiders had departed.
The G.P.O. discovered all the evacuated men taking cover in
the gun-pits.  For awhile he remained in one of the pits,
waiting like the rest of them for the explosion that could be
expected any second.  When, after a few minutes, nothing
had happened, and the first fever of excitement had cooled
down, the G.P.O. found his thoughts turning into a very
definite direction.

" It's a damn shame if we lose all our instruments . . ."
these ran.  " They're worth thousands . . . God knows when
we shall be able to get a replacement.  Spares are almost
unobtainable nowadays . . . If they go up it's quite possible
the whole gun-site will be out of action indefinitely . . ."

These reflections gently led him on a further stage.

" I must get those instruments out . . . But it's too heavy
a job for one man . . . It takes about six men to shift the
predictor alone . . ."

He jumped to his feet and placed the megaphone to his lips.

" I want volunteers to help me get the instruments out of
the Command Post," he shouted.

A profound silence followed.  In the semi-darkness no one
spoke, no one stirred.  The Gun Position Officer waited a
while and then walked from one pit to another looking at the
sheltering men, but saying no more.  After an interval four
men stepped slowly forward.

" Good fellows ! . . ." exclaimed the G.P.O. " That's enough. . . . Let's do a useful job . . ."

The G.P.O. and the four volunteers entered the predictor pit almost on tip-toe as if afraid that the mere disturbance of their tread might explode the bomb. It still stood firmly planted in the earth by the wall of the pit, enigmatic and sinister with its ugly top fin.

One of the men approached gingerly and bent down to listen.

" Can't hear anything, sir," he said in a breathless whisper.

When the first few moments had passed and they found themselves still alive their confidence began to grow. They settled down to their big job with strength and speed. Before they could consider conveying the bulky predictor out they had first to pull down part of a sand-bag blast wall. Then the five of them clustered round the instrument and by dint of much laborious pushing and lifting managed gradually to edge it through the gap. With a further long-drawn-out effort they succeeded in shifting it to a spot about fifty yards from the pit, which the G.P.O. decided, in the circumstances, was good enough. And there still remained much more to do. The five of them were sweating profusely, and sweating not entirely from their labours. As far as possible they tried to keep their minds off that grim exclamation mark in the predictor pit, and avoided looking in its direction. Barely a word was spoken all the while. Apart from the fact that most of their breath was needed for their job each of them felt disinclined to betray in speech the anxiety that beset him. And there was nothing else worth wasting words on at such a moment.

In the faint moonlight they returned, in a sort of fatalistic silence, to wrestle with the height-finder as they had done with the predictor, wondering all the time if their luck would still hold. A new air-raid had developed and all over the island the sirens were moaning. Face to face with their own imminent peril the men hardly noticed them. Then searchlights began to rove over the sky and bombs started to burst. Each explosion echoed in their ears as an unhappy reminder of one bomb that had still to burst.

At last it was over. They had lifted the height-finder and the Telescope Identification off their cement pedestals and carted them to places of safety. Their last job was to pull out of the pit the electric cable that connected the predictor to the guns.

It was an operation that afforded them a final look at the bomb. Then they turned and raced like men with Death at their heels for the cover of the gun-pits. They had stood on the brink of the Unknown for what seemed to have been an eternity, however short a time it really was.

Then the bomb exploded. Almost, it seemed, before they had had time to realise they were safe. A terrific concussion shook the air. Bits of rock, sand, and fragments of sand-bags rained down upon the gun-pits. The G.P.O., sheltering in No. 4 pit, felt someone give a yell and fall at his feet. He thought at first that a man had been hit by a flying splinter. He discovered it was the No. 3 of the predictor crew, the unfortunate—or fortunate—fellow whose foot had been trapped by the bomb. The man was quite unhurt but the shock of the explosion acting on an imagination that too vividly pictured the might-have-been, had caused him to faint. The G.P.O. told off a couple of gunners to take him to the First-Aid Post in the moat.

He felt a firm, affectionate squeeze of the arm. It was the Colonel.

" Thank God . . ." said the latter, simply.

" Yes, sir. It might have been worse," replied the G.P.O. As he spoke he knew it was a poor thing to say. But just then the fitting words did not come easily.

They walked over to examine the Command Post. It was completely smashed. But the concrete pedestals in the pits were intact. The G.P.O. ordered the Command Post staff to bring back the instruments and temporarily re-erect them among the ruins.

As the cable to the guns was being attached to the predictor the shout of the spotter was heard calling out a new bearing and angle. In a few minutes the guns were despatching their shells towards another plane momentarily illuminated in the beam of a searchlight.

The G.P.O. got through on the 'phone to Gun Operations Room.

" Pedro in action again . . ." he reported.

On the way back to R.H.Q. the Colonel decided that before going to bed that night he would send the G.P.O.'s name with a strong recommendation for the Military Cross, and the names of the four volunteers for the Military Medal.

### IX—Gunner on Parade

" WILL you be my best man, Smiler ? " Doughy ventured to ask one morning when they were doing maintenance in No. 3 gun-pit.

" Where's the reception ? " was the cautious reply.

" There won't be one . . . Nothing like José's."

" Oh . . . That makes a difference.

After a moment, seeing the shade of disappointment that darkened Doughy's solemn countenance, Smiler added :

" All right, Doughy. I'll hold your hand. But remember, I still think you're a bloody fool to get married."

It was approaching the end of April. On the day after Father Joseph's interview with the Colonel, Doughy had presented himself at the Battery Office to inform the Major that the banns were being put up. The Battery Major, faced with the *fait accompli*, wasted no further time on discussion or persuasion. Besides, in the midst of the grave and tremendous happenings of their present existence at the Fort, the fact that one gunner insisted on marrying a Maltese girl assumed a comparative insignificance, even when considered merely from the point of view of a domestic battery concern.

" When is the date of the marriage ? " asked the Major.

" It's not settled yet, sir."

" Well, let me know the instant it is and I'll have all the necessary steps taken."

" Yes, sir."

" Of course you know that in addition to the usual Army allowance of twenty-one shillings per week your wife becomes entitled to sixpence a day of your pay ? "

" Yes, sir."

" You may put in for forty-eight hours' leave for your marriage," the Major continued. " I want you to realise that apart from this you get no special privileges at all. Just the usual 24-hours' leave once a fortnight. No sleeping-out passes. You understand ? "

" Yes, sir," replied Doughy. " I'm due for my five days' leave in three weeks' time, sir."

" Excellent. That will give you a nice honeymoon. Well, Baker . . . I sincerely wish you and your bride good luck, and I hope your marriage will turn out a very happy one."

Doughy left the office with a lighter heart than had been his for months. All his troubles were over now. He knew that whatever opposition his marriage intentions had provoked in the past, henceforth it would all be forgotten. It was in Doughy's nature to desire to conform in every respect to the wishes of his superior officers. The little tussle over Carmela had given him more discomfort than he cared to show. Now he could feel at ease again.

He took a mild and modest satisfaction in reviewing the steps that had led him to this desirable stage over the long period of more than eighteen months. First his decision to give Carmela a chance to fill the gap in his life left by Sharman. Then the decision to marry her for his own security. Then to bring himself to the right mood for broaching the subject to the Battery Commander. Then his determination to become R.C. Then his determination *not* to become R.C. Then, at last, the putting-up of the banns, and the good wishes of the Battery Commander. It had all been slow and deliberate in the way he liked to do things. He had taken time to make up his mind firmly before each step. Nothing had pushed him from his purpose. And, modestly, he felt a glow of pride in his triumph.

In No. 3 gun-pit, with the exception of Smiler, it was considered in the light of a triumph, too. A triumph of tenacity of purpose over all the bad weather that is sure to blow between a man and a girl in the course of such an extensive period as eighteen months. The gun-crew hastened to give Doughy his due for sticking to it. Their explanation was that he must be " really gone " on the girl. Smiler thought so, too. None of them had penetrated Doughy's secret. They all thought the prime motive was the simple and old-fashioned one—that he wanted the girl badly. Doughy did want the girl. And badly. But not quite in the sense the gun-crew supposed.

The approaching marriage divided their interests with the blitz itself. In fact it became the popular theme in the dug-out. Living lives of such abnormality day by day amid the roar of Grand Harbour Barrage, the shattering downpour of bombs, the reek of cordite, the savage beat of Death's wings, they turned with relief to Doughy's marriage preparations as to a sane spot in a mad world.

Out of his savings Doughy had bought himself a blue gunner

walking-out dress, with blue-and-red peaked cap, to be married in. It was made to measure by a Valetta tailor whose whole life had been devoted to the construction of naval and military upholstery. And it transformed Doughy. On the wedding day he conveyed it from the dug-out, which was too cramped and dusty for the donning of such splendour, across to the Naffy canteen, part of which was now devoted to men's sleeping quarters. Here he arrayed himself and, there being no " Alert " on at the time, most of the gun-crews found an opportunity to steal over to the canteen one by one to see the sight.

The wedding was timed for three o'clock. Smiler, on the strength of being the best man, had been issued with a special twelve-hour pass by the Number One of the gun. Steve, the loader, had tried hard for a similar favour. But the sergeant was adamant.

" One's all we can spare. And we can't really spare him. Don't forget, Smiler. Twelve hours. Not twenty-four."

So Steve had to console himself with the knowledge that, in any case, there wouldn't be any beer going. Valetta, like the canteen, was practically dry.

Doughy in red-and-blue and Smiler in khaki-drill mounted their bicycles and rode off up the Melita Road. Traffic had been so badly interfered with by the incessant bombing and petrol was so scarce that troops on leave were now supplied with bicycles free, for getting about.

On arriving at the church in Floriana there was no one about. They went inside and sat waiting in a pew at the back. Oil paintings and coloured statues of the Virgin and Saints, before which white candles were burning, decorated the white plaster walls of the interior. Two colossal candles burned before the altar, and dozens of small ones in little chapels at the sides. A faint odour of incense pervaded the place. In the dim light they could see dotted about in pews and before the shrines, the figures of a dozen women or so, bowed in prayer.

Shortly after, the main door of the church swung open and Carmela herself appeared accompanied by a small crowd of relations and friends including her two needle-eyed sisters, her two aged aunts and an elderly man or two.

If Doughy in his red and blue was a revelation to Carmela, none the less was she a revelation to him. She was attired in a white silk dress with a short train, wore a wreath of little pink and white flowers on her coal black hair, and carried a spray of lilies. Doughy stared. He had never seen her in anything but black before. A queer feeling came over him.

Smiler was impressed, too.

" If she had more bridge to her nose, and her mouth wasn't so big, and she wasn't so sallow, and her eyes were farther apart, she wouldn't be bad looking," he said to himself.

Amid subdued whisperings the bridal party commenced to walk down the aisle, Doughy and Carmela in front and the relatives following. Carmela dipped her fingers in the holy water, crossed herself, saying in Maltese : " In the name of the Father and of the Son and of the Holy Ghost." Doughy thought it respectful to imitate her. They walked up the main aisle towards the altar where the bride genuflected. Doughy, watching her every movement, nervously followed suit.

From here they proceeded to the vestry. A priest, who for some reason or other was not Father Joseph, awaited them in a small room illuminated by two stained-glass windows. It was barely furnished with a desk and a couple of plain wooden chairs. Some priestly vestments hung from pegs on the wall, exuding the faint odour of sanctity peculiar to such places.

The priest put down the breviary he was reading and rose to greet the bride and bridegroom with a " *Bon giurno.*" Over his long black cotta was draped his white cassock with a foot of lace at the hem. An ivory satin stole, handsomely embroidered with gold hung from his shoulders.

He took up his position, back to the desk, with the bridal couple in front of him and the bunch of relatives standing a respectful distance behind. The service was in Maltese, so Doughy understood none of it. But he kept a corner of his eye on Carmela and whenever she crossed herself he did the same. When the priest came to the questions : " Wilt thou have this woman ? . . ." " Wilt thou have this man ? . . ." he repeated them twice, first in Maltese and then in broken English.

" Yes," said Doughy.

" *Eiva* (Yes)," replied Carmela.

" *Eiva*," added Doughy, too.

The air-raid sirens had started to wail just as they entered the vestry. Outside Grand Harbour Barrage was thundering in the skies. Occasionally a bomb fell fairly close. The little vestry shook and flakes of plaster dropped from the ceiling upon the marriage register which lay open on the desk. The priest had to shake the fragments from the page before they could sign. Carmela and Doughy wrote their names, and then Smiler, and one of the elderly men as witnesses. The registrar stood at hand to make sure it was all done correctly.

This business over the priest turned towards Carmela and delivered for her benefit a short address on the marital duties and responsibilities of a wife. Carmela listened with lowered eyes. As the address was in Maltese Doughy could understand nothing. Then his own turn came. This time the priest endeavoured to make himself clear in English. With his limited supply he found it difficult to say what he wanted to without appearing a trifle crude. Halfway through Doughy felt Smiler nudge him from behind and heard a whisper :

" Tell him you're in the R.A. and already know the facts of life."

Instead of which Doughy punctuated the priest's discourse with an occasional " *Eiva* " . . . hoping to show politely that he agreed with all that was being said.

The bridal couple knelt down. The priest spoke a short prayer, lifted up his hand and blessed them. It was all over, much to the relief of both Doughy and Smiler. They came out into the sunlight again. The sirens were announcing the " All Clear." Outside the church Doughy kissed his bride. Her sisters and the old aunts retaliated on him. And Smiler did the same with Carmela.

" It's an old English custom, if you don't happen to know, Carmela," he said.

" I like it, Smee-ler," replied Carmela with a friendly smile, leaving him not quite sure whether she meant the custom or his own application of it.

Doughy, for his first married home, had rented a cheap, small, two-roomed furnished flat in a house in a poor neighbourhood close by, which had been evacuated by the previous tenants who preferred dwelling in an air-raid shelter. Here the wedding party proceeded, Doughy and Carmela in a *carrozin*, the others following on foot behind.

Smiler's face lengthened as soon as he entered the apartment. He hadn't expected much in the way of entertainment. But he had always hoped. His hopes vanished the instant he glanced at the table. A few anchovies in oil, a few slices of pumpkin, a tomato or two, a concoction of macaroni, a couple

of Maltese loaves, and some stew that looked as if it had been
brought home from a Victory Kitchen. There was no beer, of
course. He couldn't blame Doughy for that. Valetta had been
practically dry for weeks. But what a reception, he thought
gloomily, compared with that magnificent, never-to-be-
forgotten spread at José's wedding !

He stood watching Carmela's Maltese relations crowding
round the table in the small room.

" Well, they're all yours now, Doughy," he said cynically.
" All yours. For keeps."

However, just then Doughy was a hundred-per-cent proof
against cynicism. He had been watching Carmela attending
to her duties as hostess and once or twice she had exchanged a
glance across the room with him. It was just the same sort of
glance that Doughy remembered seeing exchanged between
José and his bride on the occasion of their wedding reception.
A glance that implied tacit understanding between husband
and wife. It set the seal on Doughy's certainty that, with
Carmela belonging to him, he would never have to face that
dreary loneliness of existence which he dreaded beyond
anything else. A great contentment filled him.

Carmela went to a small cupboard and returned holding
her hands behind her. She walked across to Smiler and, with
a little laugh, flourished two bottles in front of his face. His
eyes bulged. He was staring at something he had hardly
expected ever to see again.

" Blimey . . . Blue Label ! . . . " he shouted. " Where
did you find them, Carmela ? "

" One for you. One for him," laughed Carmela, passing
over the bottles.

" Tell me where you found them, Carmela," Smiler persisted
excitedly. " They may have some more. I'll go round now."

Carmela shook her head.

" I buy them one, two . . . seven week ago," she said.
" No more. All gone."

She had purchased the Blue Labels at a bar when the
drought was beginning to be felt and had jealously hoarded
them for the present occasion.

" You ought to have bought the shop, Carmela," said
Smiler reproachfully. " Never mind. You did your best.
You're not the first girl to underestimate the size of my
thirst."

He filled his glass, held it up and gazed on the rising bubbles fondly. He felt all the pleasant sentiments of an unexpected reunion with an old friend after painful separation.

" Here's all the best, Carmela. Here's luck, Doughy."

The Blue Label disappeared without a halt.

Half an hour passed. Smiler edged Doughy outside the room.

" Look here, Doughy," he said earnestly. " That Blue Label's given me a big thirst. And a big idea. What say we have a run round and see if we can get on the track of some more ? I've nine hours leave left and I'm going to comb out this town before I go back."

Doughy looked dumb.

" I couldn't leave Carmela," he said slowly, after a pause.

" Who's asking you to ? She can come as well. Seems to me she has a useful nose for Blue Labels. Besides, you've got to do something to pass the time till night."

Once more Doughy went wooden while he turned the idea over and over in his mind. He suffered no craving for " Blues " himself. On the other hand he didn't fancy being left alone by Smiler for the evening to entertain his new Maltese relations.

" I'll ask Carmela," he said.

In a few minutes he reappeared.

" She'll come," he announced. " She's gone to change her frock."

## X—IN SEARCH OF BLUE LABEL

CARMELA rejoined them in due course, hatless and again clad in black. Leaving the relations in possession the three of them descended into the street.

" First thing is to hire Carmela a bike," said Smiler.

They managed to do this at a shop kept by a friend of José. Then, under Smiler's professional guidance they commenced to scour the city for Blue Labels. They combed the Strada Stretta and the side streets. North, south, east, and west. Sometimes they could ride for a few hundred yards. But very often they had to dismount and lift their bicycles over the heaps of ruins blocking the roadways. Smiler led them into all sorts of alleys, many of which were unknown to Carmela herself. All the others did was to follow him docilely. He doubled up and down the streets, concentrated on one idea alone, like a bloodhound on the trail. It was hot and disappointing work. Many of Smiler's pet bars were closed for good. They tried the Cardiff Bar in the Marsa. It had no Blue Label. Only the ambiguous " ambeet " which Smiler wouldn't look at. At the Dewdrop Inn they had no better luck. Nor at the Lord Nelson.

At the end of an hour Smiler halted, perspiring, and with a worried expression.

" Something's gone wrong," he said. " Just let me think."

Doughy and Carmela sat down on some bomb debris and patiently awaited the result of their generalissimo's consultation with himself.

" Let me see . . ." considered Smiler. " We might sound the Europa. That's in Palace-square at the top of the Stretta. Or there's the Premier. Both of them might have some beer. But they charge more than at a pub. . . . I think we'll leave them to the last. Now, let me see . . . What haven't we tried ? "

Suddenly he jumped to his feet.

" The Balaclava . . ." he said. " That's the place. Come on."

The Balaclava was a small bar in the dockyard area kept by a little, fat, bald-headed Maltese known as Billy. When the three arrived they found the shutters up. Smiler swore loudly. But the Balaclava proved on closer inspection to be open after all. Smiler led them through a swing-door into a small room with a few tables and chairs and a plentiful carpeting of cigarette stubs and match ends on the wooden floor. The place was empty save for the bald-headed proprietor standing behind the bar.

" *Bon giurno*, Billy," exlaimed Smiler.

" Ah, Meester Smiler . . . Pleased to see you some more. You not been here long time," replied Billy, welcoming his old customer.

" Three Blue Labels . . . Quick . . ." ordered Smiler, as if there was no such thing as a drought on.

Billy remained with his elbows on the bar. An expansive and deprecating smile spread over his fat countenance.

" What's the joke ? " demanded Smiler.

" Ah, Meester Smiler. You know. The beer ? It is not."

" You're a cunning old liar, Billy. I know you're not dry. Come on . . . Bottles up."

Billy lifted his shoulders in an expressive shrug.  His smile grew more expansive than ever.

" Ambeet," he suggested.

" To hell with ' ambeet '," exclaimed Smiler.

For a moment he felt baffled.  Then he had an idea.

" See these two," he said, denoting Doughy and Carmela. " Just got married.  Show him your ring, Carmela."

" Ah, married," said Billy, beaming on the pair.  " That is good."

" Good ! . . . We know it's good," exclaimed Smiler. " But it will be a damned sight better with a Blue Label. Marriage is thirsty work.  Go on, Billy."

After considerable persuasion Billy removed his elbows from the bar.

" All right," he said genially.  " I go and see.  But I know there is nothing."

In a minute or two he returned carrying one bottle of Blue Label.  " It was hiding," he explained.  " In the dark. I not see it before.  It is the luck for the bride."

" Luck ! . . . One bottle ! . . . What about the others ? " said Smiler.

" No more," replied Billy, shaking his head decisively. And Smiler felt it was useless to persist.

They divided the Blue Label into three glasses.  Smiler tossed his share off at a gulp.

The swing-door opened again.  There entered an elderly Maltese wearing a dirty cap, a white-shirt blouse and a pair of narrow blue-jean trousers with ragged ends reaching some inches from his ankles.  He was bare-footed and walked with a limp, dragging his left foot along the floor like a broom, and sweeping the rubbish on the floor into little heaps. This odd-looking character was followed into the bar by a goat.

" Two squirts," said Billy in Maltese, handing the newcomer a yellow china jug.

The man with the limp knelt down beside the goat and milked it into the jug, while the animal placidly gobbled up all the cigarette ends and bits of paper within reach.  When the operation was over Billy paid the milkman a few pence and poured him out a glass of " ambeet " which he swallowed with a grunt of thanks.  The goat began to make droppings on the floor of the bar.

Billy informed Smiler that before the war the man owned a herd of a dozen goats. This one was the sole survivor. All over the island it was the same. The 30,000 goat-population of Malta had almost disappeared since the siege began. Government House, said Billy, had promised to compensate the goat-keepers for their losses after the war by supplying the island with Welsh goats of a better quality than the home product.

The limping man turned to depart. As he left the bar, dragging the goat behind him, he dexterously swept up its droppings with the side of his lame naked foot, guided them through the door, and deposited them in the street.

" Glad I'm not eating," said Doughy.

Like Smiler he had finished his share of the Blue Label. Carmela had only sipped hers. Suddenly she offered her glass to Smiler.

" For you, Smee-ler," she said, prettily.

The temptation was great. But Smiler hesitated.

" No, Carmela," he said. " That's yours. It wouldn't be fair. I've had my share. Go on, finish it."

" For you," she insisted again.

" Well, if you don't want it . . ."

He poured the gift down his throat.

" Doughy," he said, moved to conviction, " you've got something good in Carmela."

The sirens began to wail outside, and when the barrage started Billy closed the bar and went to a shelter. Outside in the street Smiler said gloomily :

" One bottle . . . We haven't done much good so far. No use in hanging about in Valetta now. All the bars have closed down. They won't open again till the " All Clear." And that may be hours."

He considered the situation for a while.

" Let's get on our bikes and go to Luzza," he suggested finally. It's only a couple of miles away. I know a little place there. It hasn't got a name, but I call it Jimmie's. The daughter of the house is an old pal of mine. I can have anything I want when I want it. And if they've got any beer it won't be hiding in the dark. They keep the barrels on the floor and draw it up through a rubber tube. You game, Carmela ? Not afraid of the raid ? "

Since her association with Doughy she had overcome a

considerable part of her former dread.  But she was by no means without fear.  However, she agreed to the proposal. They mounted their cycles and rode off, taking the way through the ruined streets of Senglea.  They had not proceeded more than six hundred yards when a stick of bombs fell amongst the buildings on their right.  The blast blew the three of them off their machines.  Picking himself up with a cut forehead Smiler was relieved to find Doughy and Carmela uninjured.  His own cycle had sustained a badly buckled front wheel.  Fortunately, further along the street was the shop from which they had hired Carmela's cycle.  The proprietor agreed to do the repairs to the damaged machine and, meanwhile to loan Smiler another one.  Once more they started, deafened by the din of Grand Harbour Barrage, bursting bombs and falling buildings, and covered with the powdery dust from the pulverised limestone.  Soon Doughy's splendid new red-and-blue could hardly be distinguished from Smiler's khaki drill.

At last the houses ended.  They entered open country parcelled out into small cultivated fields divided by stone walls two feet high.  There was hardly a flat patch of any dimension.  The ground continually rose and dropped in shallow terraces.  It was a treeless landscape except for the presence of an occasional dull-green, bushy karab-tree.  The raid had banished all sign of activity.

After leaving the last houses behind them they were just in time to see a parachute gracefully disposing of itself three fields away on their left.

" What's on the end of that ?  A Jerry ? " exclaimed Smiler.  " Hold my bike, Doughy, while I reconnoitre."

All three dismounted.  Smiler drew his jack-knife jumped over the low wall by the roadside and crept towards the field where lay the parachute.

In a few minutes he returned.

" Don't see any sign of a Jerry," he said.

For a moment they all stood gazing at the white heap.

" That's silk, you know," said Smiler.  " Worth quite a bit . . . Carmela, how would you like a wedding present ? Make yourself a frock."

" I would like," nodded Carmela.

" It's yours."

He started back to where the parachute lay.  Hardly had

he taken a couple of steps when he was surprised by the roar of
an aeroplane engine. A Ju. 88 was diving out of the clouds
right above his head. He yelled back to Doughy and Carmela
to take cover, and hurled himself to the ground again. The
Ju. 88 dropped down to a hundred and fifty feet. The rush of
air beat upon Smiler like the gust of a storm. He saw five
bombs drop. They came nearer and nearer. The last exploded
less than fifty yards from where he lay, covering him with
earth and stones.

When all was quiet again he rose to his feet more determined
than ever to get Carmela her wedding present. He worked
his way across the two fields.

Then he stopped and stared. Where the parachute had
been was now a smoking bomb crater. Carmela's wedding
present had received a direct hit. Tiny fragments of it lay
scattered over the field, not one big enough to make a
pocket-handkerchief of. He rejoined his companions.

" No good, Carmela," he said, laconically. " Jerry beat
me to it. I'll have to save up and buy you something.
After the war . . ."

The barrage seemed to be dying down a little and the
explosion of bombs in the Three Cities behind them became
less frequent.

" Let's hurry up to Jimmie's. We've wasted enough time
already," said Smiler. " I want to get there before the " All
Clear," Doughy. My girl's parents always go to the shelter
when a raid is on. She stays in the bar. She pretends to
them that she's brave. But what she really does it for is to
have the chance of a bit of time alone with any bloke like
me that drops in. Come on. Double up . . ."

Very shortly they reached Jimmie's. As Smiler had
predicted the parents were absent in the shelter and his
girl friend had the place to herself. Except for the barrels
on the floor the bar might have been a room in a private
house.

" Three beers," demanded Smiler, confidently, when the
greetings were over.

" No beer. All gone," replied the girl.

Unable to believe her Smiler went over to the barrels and
gave each of them a powerful kick. Their hollow response
told its own tale.

" Can you beat it ? " he exclaimed in utter disgust.

Then he began to look on the bright side.

" Now I am here I may as well start a bit of square-pushing,"
he said with a grin. " What do you say, Doughy, to you, me,
Carmela and her making a foursome ? "

## XI—One Sunday on the Gun-site

IN the Naffy canteen the visiting padre was preparing for
Divine Service. It should have taken place in the morning.
But a long " Alert," including three successive raids, had
pinned the troops to the guns. So the padre stayed on,
hoping for a lull. It wasn't till half-past two in the afternoon
that, for the moment, there were no " plots " on the board
in the Command Post and the men had time to eat their
dinner.

The Naffy canteen was installed in the larger of the two
remaining " cavaliers " at the Fort that had escaped bomb
damage. This ancient vault extended for about thirty feet
into the limestone rock, with an arched roof, ten-feet high
in the centre. Ceiling and sides still preserved the rough-
hewn condition in which they had existed for centuries.
A few kits belonging to troops who slept in the Naffy for
want of other quarters were laid out alongside the walls.
The trestle tables had been folded up and a gunner was
arranging the canteen benches in rows ready for the congregation. From the sunny afternoon outside a broad shaft
of vivid light penetrated through the open doorway of the
" cavalier," brilliantly illuminating half of it and leaving the
far end in a sort of cool twilight.

Across the centre of the Naffy counter, over which, in more
luscious days, the Blue Label had been wont to circulate so
freely, the padre had spread a crimson altar cloth on top of
an army blanket. He carried this altar cloth around with
him to the various gun-sites on Sundays, and had not been
quite successful in smoothing out the creases of the folds.
In the middle stood a small brass crucifix, flanked on either
side by two glass tumblers filled with bunches of *ingliza*, a
yellow flower, something like a small Michaelmas daisy, that
grows all over the island. A small silver chalice covered with
a folded napkin, and a silver plate containing tiny cubes of

bread on a white cloth, were placed in front of the crucifix. Behind the improvised altar the canteen shelves spread themselves, bare and empty. They had been cleared of all their allurements to the flesh though, in truth, these nowadays were very feeble indeed, and consisted chiefly of empty bottles, unused glasses and dummy cigarette cartons, none of which was likely to distract the minds of the congregation from more spiritual matters, unless by stimulating melancholy comparisons with the days before Naffy had gone dry. But the padre thought it best to be on the safe side.

The gunner had just finished placing at intervals on the benches the well-thumbed sheets containing the order of Divine Service and the hymns, when the troops began to file in, removing their tin-hats as they crossed the threshold. Leaving the first row free for the officers they subsided into their seats, tired after the exhausting morning and very much inclined to doze. Most of them had enjoyed little beyond interrupted snatches of sleep for months. In the curious mixed light diffused within the " cavalier " their faces, despite the tan of the sun, appeared drawn and careworn. They filled only ten or so of the benches. Almost as many men again were kept away by duties at the gun-site, or had been detailed for ammunition fatigues.

There was a shuffling of feet as the tired men rose to their feet again. Led by the Colonel, who had driven over from new R.H.Q. outside the Fort, the little group of officers entered and took their places in the front row. Before the altar, hymn book in hand, stood the sturdy padre, his sensible face faintly betraying satisfaction that at last he was getting his show. Beneath the hem of his cassock showed glimpses of the webbing gaiters of his battle-dress. A purple stole draped each side of his surplice, embroidered at one end with the regimental crest and on the other with the monogram C.F. (Chaplain to the Forces). He paused for a second or two to rivet attention and then announced :

" We will join in singing Hymn No. 4 on the sheet :

" *Fight the good fight with all thy Might ;*
" *Christ is thy Strength and Christ thy Right . . .*"

There was a scraping of ammunition boots as everyone rose. The bench on which Doughy sat next to Smiler got

knocked over on to the feet of the men in the row behind.
When order was restored the padre gave the signal to start
with a beat of his hand. At first he had the singing all to
himself. Without the cover of music everyone felt self-
conscious. But the padre possessed an excellent baritone
voice. The hymn sounded good, which encouraged the
congregation gradually to chime in. At the end they were all
singing heartily, and the " Amen " was loud enough to be
heard away in the gun-pits.

The simple service followed, including a Lesson which the
Colonel read with emphatic pauses between the sentences,
somewhat in the manner in which he detailed orders. Then
came another hymn :

> " Rock of Ages, cleft for me,
>    Let me hide myself in Thee . . ."

After which, the padre had a few announcements to make.
A new series of Confirmation classes was starting.

" I shall be visiting this site every Tuesday evening. Will
all those who wish to attend the class hand in their names at
the Battery Office . . ."

" There will be celebration of Holy Communion at the end
of the service. Those desiring to celebrate please remain
behind . . ."

On the previous day the gun-site had once more been
visited by death. In the middle of a raid a back-fire occurring
on the unlucky No. 2 gun blew out the breech and killed
three men. The gun was now out of action.

The padre had designed his service to be in the
nature of a memorial to the victims. He chose as his
text, St. John iii, 16.

> " For God so loved the world, that He gave His only
> begotten Son, that whosoever believeth in Him
> should not perish, but have everlasting life."

The padre preached on the Life to come, the inner meaning
of Death to the true Christian, the promise of the grave.
It was a simple, manly sermon, strong in affirmation and
untroubled by perplexities. Its power lay in the sincerity of
the preacher. The men listened with serious faces. They

felt conscious of the solemnity of the occasion. Since the bombing of gun-sites had become a German habit, they had suffered the loss of many of their comrades. The Fort itself was three-quarters devastated. They dwelt and fought among craters and ruins. The air attacks grew fiercer every day. For a whole month the aerodromes had been practically out of action. The entire weight of the attack had fallen on the gunners. Alone, they shot down over a hundred planes in those four weeks. But it made little difference. The Luftwaffe continued to darken the skies, two or three hundred bombers at a time escorted by scores of fighters. The gun-sites themselves became individual targets and the casualty lists rose higher and higher. At such times, in order to lighten the strain upon the men the authorities despatched A.R.P. personnel or troops from infantry regiments to the afflicted gun-site so as to avoid the grim business of having friends digging out friends. But this was not always possible. There was too much to do of the same nature in Valetta itself.

The feeling that they were cut off from the outside world and had no one to depend on but themselves increased daily. No convoys could get through. This sense of isolation was deepened by the utter absence of letters and newspapers from home. Their dependence on the wireless merely emphasised the fact.

Dark days were succeeded by darker days. And the future looked blacker still. By way of contrast, the hardships of a few months previously became invested in the memory of the Fort Pedro gunners with the glow of happy retrospect—the halcyon time when it was still possible to have pork on Christmas Day and the Hurricane had come over and bombarded the site with paper streamers. . . . Now, they could not rid themselves of the oppressive anxiety that events were rapidly piling-up towards some tremendous dénouement. It needed very little imagination for them to realise they were living amid big uncertainties, from hour to hour. All this lent a special personal interest to the padre's discourse. All this rendered it grimly topical to them.

Doughy had come to the service with his mind entirely occupied by the golden fact that in three hours' time his five days' leave would start and he would pass through the gates of the Fort to begin his honeymoon with Carmela. When the padre was leading them in the hymns and prayers Doughy's thoughts roamed far from heavenly affairs. But even his attention was eventually arrested by the earnest and solemn words of the padre's discourse. He listened on, forgetting Carmela 'for the moment.

" When dead, there is an after-life . . . Friends will meet friends ! "

The padre's closing words rang out with all the intensity of conviction, echoing in the hush that had enveloped the vault. The closing hymn was announced. It was one that took Doughy back to his far-off orphanage days, and after a few moments he found himself singing with fervour.

" *Abide with me, fast falls the eventide,*
" *The darkness deepens ; Lord, with me abide . . .".*

Then, after " God Save the King," they filed out into the bright sunlight again. A subaltern and five gunners remained behind for Communion.

" Air Observe ! . . ."

The shout rang out from the Command Post. A new raid was impending. Dismissing their devotions from their minds the gunners raced to the gun-pits, spurred by the shouts of the sergeants.

" Imshi ! . . . Double-up ! . . . Imshi ! . . ."

Alone with his six communicants the padre proceeded to deliver the Body and the Blood while the guns of Grand Harbour Barrage roared its unholy accompaniment.

Perched in his layer's seat in No. 3 gun-pit Smiler gave the necessary little turns to the dial handle of the 3.7's traversing gear, humming as he did so, " Abide with me " . . .

The raid was a comparatively light one. There was no further interruption to the Sunday peace for some time. The gunners cleaned the guns, replenished the ammunition. They had just finished when the cooks appeared on the bridge over the moat, bringing up tea.

Tea and—tinned salmon ! It was such a surprise that it put the men in a happier frame of mind than had been theirs for many a long meal-time. There wasn't much of it, but coming unexpectedly after unadulterated weeks of bully beef and M. and V., their spirits rose accordingly. Doughy, whose leave had just begun, couldn't resist the temptation to stay-on for a last meal at the Fort. He squatted down with his mess-tin beside Smiler chatting about what he and Carmela intended doing with their five days' honeymoon. The first half was to be spent at the flat in Floriana, and then they were going on a bicycle trip to the other side of the island.

"Almost makes marriage pay," observed Smiler with a grin. He rose to his feet. "I'm going to the lats. I've been taken short. Hang around, Doughy, for a bit in case there's a call. I won't be long."

He hurried off and had scarcely disappeared when the Alert whistles blew. The gun-crews washed down the tinned salmon with a last mouthful of tea and dashed into the gun-pits.

"Where's Smiler ? ? " bellowed the sergeant of No. 3 gun.

"In the lats.," said Doughy. "I'll stand in."

"Thought you were on leave."

"So I am. But it don't matter for a bit."

He mounted the vacant layer's seat on No. 3 gun and began to occupy himself with the traversing gear.

In the Command Post the telephonist was waiting for the plots to come in from Gun Operations Room.

"Blimey ! . . ." he exclaimed suddenly.

His shock was caused by the voice at the far end of the wire announcing that it was a 300-plus raid. The telephonist entered the ominous figure on his A.K. message form together with further information.

"Bearing, One-five degrees. . . ."

"Range, Thirty-thousand. . . ."

Rapidly the Tactical Control Officer worked out the plot on his board and gave the Gun Position Officer the angle for the guns.

"Go to bearing, One-O degrees," shouted the G.P.O., and the guns traversed to meet the new storm.

The Tactical Control Officer was soon confronted with a new task. The original plot split up as the raiders approached Malta, one formation coming in the direction of the gun-site from the Sliema direction, the other striking a course for Valetta.

"50-plus . . . One-O degrees . . . 15,000 . . .," announced the telephonist.

And immediately afterwards :

" 250-plus . . . Two-O degrees . . . 15,000."

The T.C.O. commenced to rule and measure again. It was soon very apparent to him that the 50-plus plot was coming straight for them.

" Bearing, One-five degrees . . . 15,000 . . ." he shouted to the Gun Position Officer.

" Go to bearing One-five," the G.P.O. ordered the guns anew, and the instruments in the Command Post pit also went to revised bearing.

All over the island the warning sirens were rising and falling in their dreary wail. On the gun-site there descended a quietness, like the pause before a whirlwind breaks. The G.P.O. stood close to the spotter, both staring through their glasses out to sea.

" Plane ! . . ." suddenly yelled the G.P.O.

" Ju. 88," added the spotter.

And even as they looked they saw the 50-plus formation split up again. One series in waves of five continued towards them from Sliema. The other made a curved sweep out to sea as if towards Valetta.

" We look as though we may get it from two directions," said the Gun Position Officer, considering what he should do in that event since No. 2 gun, which had had the breech blown out the previous day, was still out of action. He decided to engage the main target with Nos. 3 and 4 and hold No. 1 for emergencies.

Calmly and unhurried the usual routine went on. At the telescope identification the spotter read the bearing and angle of sight of the bombers coming in from Sliema and passed the information to the predictor and height-finder.

" Predictor on target. . . ."

" Height-finder on target. . . ."

The shouts of the two Numbers One sounded in unison.

" First, twelve thousand . . ." called out the bombardier at the height-finder.

" Set twelve thousand . . ." shouted the Gun Position Officer to the predictor pit.

" Twelve-thousand set, sir," came the reply.

The island sirens had ceased to wail. Around and above the air throbbed and throbbed with the beat of the bombers' engines. Some of the gun-sites were already in action. By comparison with all this menacing roar the Pedro gun-site appeared for the moment an oasis of peace and tranquility. Outside No 3 gun-pit hovered Smiler who had rushed to the gun at the first opportunity in the hope of releasing Doughy, only to be told by the No. 1 to " get to hell out of the way." He knew it was impossible to change places now the guns were in action. But he hung around hoping; and feeling a little guilty of having been the means of curtailing Doughy's leave.

" Vertical steady. . . ."

" Lateral steady. . . ."

As the reports came from the predictor pit the Gun Position Officer ordered :

" Fire ! . . ."

" Fuse Two-two," shouted the No. 4 on the predictor and the G.P.O. yelled the figure through his megaphone to the waiting guns. The shells were taken from the racks and the breeches swung to behind them.

For a few seconds the gun-site seemed once more to be the only spot on earth that wasn't in violent eruption. In the calm the No. 4 on the predictor kept his eyes glued to the curve of his fuse dial, awaiting the right moment.

" Fire ! . . ." he called out, suddenly.

" Fire ! . . ." roared the Gun Position Officer's megaphone to the guns.

And instantaneously the little oasis of calm and quiet added its mite of thunder to the general welter of the pandemonium around.

Only No. 3 and No. 4 guns had fired. Watching the formation of Ju. 88's that was approaching from Sliema the G.P.O. saw all the preparations for the beginning of a shallow dive. It heartened him a bit to notice one plane fall out with smoke pouring from it. The din grew to colossal dimensions. Guns were hammering away in every direction. Junkers formations continued to come in from the sea in wave after wave.

" Eleven - thousand . . . ten - thousand . . . Nine-five hundred . . ." the No. 1 at the height-finder chanted automatically as the range diminished.

" Fuse Two-O . . ." called the No. 4 from the predictor pit.

Throwing a glance at the shell-riddled sky towards Valetta the Gun Position Officer saw something that caused him to

suck in his breath fiercely. The formation of Ju. 88's that
had broken off from the original fifty and swept, out to sea
was now flying in waves towards them. There was no
mistaking the danger. Both formations were now converging
on the gun-site. He shouted through the megaphone to
No. 1 gun :
  " Go to bearing, One-eight-O . . . Gun Control . . ."
The gun began to fire at the newcomers, independent of
further orders.
The Gun Position Officer thought the time had come to let
people know what they•might expect. And also, what was
expected of them. He raised the megaphone to his lips and
spoke in the matter - of - fact tone of normal conversation,
but slowly and clearly, so that all on the gun - site should
hear.
  " This is a deliberate attack on us . . . More so than ever
before . . . Steady, everybody . . . And we'll knock 'em
down to hell. . . ."
The words had hardly left him when the first bombs fell
from the formation that had passed over Sliema. Five waves
of five Ju. 88's apiece flew above their heads each plane
dropping one bomb. Twenty-five' bombs came screaming
down one after the other. A few fell into the sea. The
majority on the gun-site, around the gun-pits and on other
parts of the Fort. The effect of the explosions was staggering.
The very foundations of the Fort shook violently. In the
Command Post the instruments were flung from their plat-
forms. Amid the confusion and the uproar the Gun Post
Officer saw the No. 2 of the predictor, moved blindly by the
instinct for protection, snatch the canvas cover of the
predictor from the ground and bury his head in it. The
G.P.O. gave a short laugh. Even in that deadly moment it
struck him as funny.
Thud, thud, thud, hammered the bombs. A great cloud of
limestone dust enveloped the Fort like a thick yellow fog.
It was so thick that the flashes from the muzzles of the guns
as they fired became almost as red as at night. The men
groped about, choking, like apparitions.
  " Keep on firing . . . Whatever happens," the G.P.O.
roared to the guns through the din.
In the middle of it all the second formation arrived. The
gunners could no longer see the planes because of the thick

dust-cloud overhead. But they could hear the whine of the falling bombs.

Another gigantic earthquake . . . Again the Fort rocked. Amid the pall of dust and smoke the bombs exploded with a bloodshot glare like the sun in a November fog. It became more and more difficult to breathe. Bomb splinters and pieces of rock flew through the air in all directions. One cut a great hole in the predictor casing. But as the planes couldn't be seen through the fog the predictor had already stopped working.

No. 1 gun could still be heard firing " Gun Control," though aimlessly. There was no sound of firing from the other two pits.

Suddenly through the fog the Gun Position Officer discerned the shadowy figure of the sergeant on No. 4 gun standing outside the pit.

" No. 3 pit on fire, sir," he shouted, hoarsely.

Dive-bombers could now be heard screaming down and the bombs continued to burst. The fog grew denser and denser. At last the G.P.O. gave it up as hopeless.

" Stop firing ! . . ." he shouted. " Everybody report on the roadway in front of the Command Post."

In a few moments crouching figures could be seen through the fog emerging from the gun-pits and darting towards the Command Post. One man tumbled into a smoking bomb crater, crawled out again, and limped on with a broken ankle. The G.P.O. waited a few moments while the sweating, begrimed and bloodstained men silently formed up in a couple of rows before him.

Another stick of bombs fell on the gun-pits. Afterwards came the sound of the ammunition exploding in No. 3 gun-pit.

" Any men here from No. 3 gun-pit ? " the Gun Position Officer asked anxiously.

Silence.

" Take a dozen men and get some water to put out the fire," he said to the Tactical Control Officer and a subaltern. " The rest of you come along with me. Stretcher-bearers ! . . "

While the T.C.O. hurried off to fill buckets, dixies from the cookhouse and even jugs with water from a tap in the court-yard of the Fort, the Gun Position Officer led his rescue-party through the fog and dust and falling bombs to No. 3 gun-pit.

The pit had received a direct hit during the first shower of bombs. All save two of the crew were dead. The No. 1 was stretched at the entrance to the pit, a great hole in his stomach. The others of the dead were lying in the pit at their positions round the gun. The explosion had ripped the clothes off them and their bodies were blackened with soot and dust. The gun, though badly damaged, still pointed upwards, with a round in the loading tray. Steve, the loader, had fallen dead across the tray. Doughy and the other layer were sprawled backwards in their layers' seats, lifeless. The No. 4, whose duty it was to fire the gun, was crumpled up on one of the gun legs as though he had gently subsided into a soft heap where he stood. The two wounded men were groaning in pain, riddled with holes.

The Gun Position Officer, himself the first inside, dragged one of the wounded men out. The camouflage net was alight, the ammunition still exploding, and the pit reeked with the mixed stench of cordite fumes, oil, and blood. Under the G.P.O.'s inspiration the men toiled heroically to stamp out the flames, but were forced to retire.

At last the Tactical Control Officer arrived with the water party. He came on the scene just as the G.P.O. decided to dash in and make another effort to remove the second wounded man. The T.C.O. followed to help him, leaving the men to throw water on the burning sand-bags near the ammunition rack.

There came a flash and an explosion from the rack. The Gun Position Officer turned in time to see the T.C.O. reel and stagger in the gloom. He caught him from falling and, doing so, shuddered at the sight of the bleeding stump where, an instant before, had been a strong left arm.

The G.P.O. dragged him outside and laid him on a stretcher. Two gunners ran inside the pit and pulled the other wounded man out. He died as they did so.

Through the fog another man dashed frantically into the pit, oblivious of the exploding ammunition. It was Smiler. When the first bombs had began to fall, thinking it was folly to expose himself uselessly, he had retired from his position outside No. 3 gun pit and sought shelter in a " cavalier." It was from the water-party that he first heard that No. 3 gun crew were missing.

He entered the blazing pit, glanced round, and uttered an inarticulate cry. He saw Steve, his old drinking crony in the

M*                    179

bars of half the globe, lying dead over the loading-tray. But it was on Doughy that his eyes were fastened in horror. He stared at the half-naked, blackened body bewildered.

" It ought to have been me . . . Doughy took my place . . . It ought to have been me . . ." he began to shout.

No one paid the slightest attention to him. Everyone was too occupied with his own task.

## XII—EVACUATION

THE Junkers departed. The usual unnatural stillness that follows a dive-bombing attack filled the air. The fog slowly lightened. Daylight began to dawn upon them once more from the sun and blue skies overhead. The fire in No. 3 gun-pit was extinguished, and the dead laid outside.

" Call a roll, sergeant-major," the Gun Position Officer ordered.

While this was being done he checked up on the damage in the pits. Not only was No. 3 gun out of action. Numbers 1 and 4 had also been badly knocked about. Both these pits had received direct hits in the second deluge, just after the crews had been ordered to report to the Command Post. The only pit untouched was No. 2 whose gun had been rendered useless by the backfire on the day before.

'" All present, sir," announced the sergeant-major.

The death-roll had been confined to No. 3 pit. Apart from that three other gunners only had received slight shrapnel wounds.

The Gun Position Officer, himself a blackened scarecrow, ran his eye over the grimed and sooty muster.

" Take the men down to the cook-house, if it's still there, sergeant-major," he said. " Get the cooks to lay on some cocoa."

He strode across to the Command-Post telephone and got through to the Gun Control Officer at G.O.R.

" G.P.O. Pedro site speaking, sir," he said. " We've had a deliberate attack. Direct hits on three guns . . . Seven killed and four wounded."

As he relinquished the 'phone he felt a hand on his shoulder. It was the Colonel who with the Battery Commander had been at the new regimental H.Q. in the house on the Melita Road when the attack occurred, and had driven up, fearing the worst.

" Glad to see some of you are left," said the Colonel. " What happened ? "

The Gun Position Officer stood before him, red-eyed, drawn, smeared with sweat and blood and dust, making an effort to shape his words.

" All right, Bruce," interrupted the Colonel, patting him on the arm. " It will do later on. You go down immediately to my car at the gate of the Fort. In the pocket of my greatcoat you'll find a flask of brandy. Give yourself a big taste of it."

The Gun Position Officer stumbled off. Accompanied by the Battery Commander the Colonel made a tour of the Fort. The ruin was indescribable. Hardly a building remained recognisable. The three gun-pits that had received direct hits were completely wrecked. Bomb holes yawned at every step. Even the fine old gateway at the top of the steps leading from the ramparts to the sea had been destroyed.

They walked back towards the cook house, one of the buildings that had suffered least. A burst of cheering greeted them as they approached what had been the Naffy canteen. Among the ruins the men had discovered a long-overlooked box of woodbines. The cigarettes were damp and mouldy but they were being smoked with all the exquisite enjoyment of the finest cigar.

The Colonel watched them in thoughtful silence for nearly a minute.

" These fellows have been through hell," he said at last. " Day after day . . . And to-day has been the limit. In the last month our casualties must have been higher than at any other site on the island . . . They're pretty shaken up, I can see. They want a rest, or we'll be having a lot of shell shock cases . . . In any event, we haven't a gun to fire. I'm going to 'phone up Gun Operations."

In the car he found the Gun Position Officer asleep after the strain of the afternoon. The Colonel forebore to wake him, and carried him back in the car to Regimental H.Q.

At the shattered Fort ambulances arrived and took away the wounded. The dead were wrapped in blankets and conveyed in lorries to the mortuary.

On the dust-covered table in his roofless office the Battery Commander found seven little heaps with labels on top.

"Personal belonging of the casualties, sir," said the sergeant-major. "Bombardier Harris is waiting outside, sir. He's a friend of Gunner Baker. He wants to know if he can be allowed to hand Gunner Baker's things over to his widow personally, when he has his twenty-four hours' leave to-morrow."

"Baker? That's the man who got married recently, isn't it?"

"Yes, sir. He should have started his five-days' leave this afternoon, but stood-in for the bombardier on No. 3 gun at the last moment."

"Very sad, indeed," said the Major, sincerely. "Poor girl . . . Yes, sergeant-major. I think it's a good idea. It may soften the blow a bit before the official notification comes. Let the bombardier have them. No money, of course. Or valuables, like watches. And he'd better see that he gets a receipt for everything he hands over."

From the little pile on the table that was labelled "Gunner Baker," the sergeant-major selected an imitation silver cigarette case, gaudily enamelled, that had been Carmela's wedding present, a few of her letters, a cheap self-propelling pencil, a bad snapshot of Carmela, and one or two other trifles. He went outside and handed them to Smiler.

"Mind you get a receipt," he said.

Half an hour later the Colonel rang up the Battery Commander.

"I've been through to G.O.R.," he said. "It has been decided that the Pedro gun-site shall be out of action from to-night, and that the personnel are to be moved at once to the Ravioli site, the other side of the island. Will you make all preparations to move at seven-thirty. I'll send you the necessary transport."

In the gathering dusk a little column of Scammel lorries and a Matador drew up in the courtyard of the Fort. The business of departure began. Everything that was transportable was loaded up. The cook-house utensils, the tins of M and V, and bully beef, the Battery Office documents, dossiers, and typewriter, the Major's favourite chair, and the Gun Position Officer's tennis rackets which in happier days had volleyed so devastatingly on the courts at Sliema. The work proceeded in almost a silence except for the orders of the sergeants. Hardly an unnecessary word was spoken. Whatever were the feelings among Don-Troop at leaving the home where for so long they had suffered so much and enjoyed so much, each man kept his to himself. They displayed neither joy nor sorrow. The shock of the afternoon seemed to have numbed them to indifference.

Halfway through the removal the Colonel drove up. He stood for a while watching the packing-up. Then he sauntered off alone through the desolation and mounted the ramparts of the Fort. It had always been his favourite spot for an evening pipe. Once more he looked across the harbour, as he had done so often before, and admired the twilight filling the narrow streets of Valetta with rich purple shadows. The blue sea was darkening. The eastern sky was taking on the dark velvet of nightfall. Everything seemed for the moment beautiful and at peace.

The Colonel recalled how from that very spot fifteen months before, in just such a similar twilight, he had watched the unconquered *Illustrious* steal out of harbour from behind Fort St. Elmo. He remembered saying to himself : " There goes a bit of victory . . ."

He turned away from Valetta and gazed across at his own shattered gun-pits.

" And there, I suppose, is a bit of defeat," he reflected, with a wry smile. " Well, that's the way of things. In-and-out . . . One just has to take the one with the other, as they come, and go on with the job . . ."

In the courtyard Smiler was dodging about to find an opportunity for a word with the Battery sergeant-major who was superintending the loading of the vehicles. He had already repented of his desire to convey Doughy's belongings to Carmela himself. He couldn't face her, after having been the means of sending Doughy to his death. Ever since he had stood in the corpse-filled gun-pit a couple of sentences had been drumming in his memory. They were the closing words of the padre's discourse, suddenly brought to life in Smiler's mind by the disaster in letters of fire.

" *When dead there is an after-life . . . Friends will meet friends.*"

But he didn't want to meet Doughy. No more than he wanted to face Carmela. Not that Doughy would complain.

He'd just look at him in that solemn-faced way of his. . . .

At last he found his chance.

" Here's Gunner Baker's things, sergeant-major," he said holding out a handkerchief in which he had tied the relics of his friend. " Now we're moving, I shan't be going into Valetta to-morrow."

" Keep 'em for a bit," replied the sergeant-major impatiently. " Can't you see I'm up to my eyes . . . Give 'em to me to-night when we get to Ravioli."

At last it was finished. The lorries laden with equipment moved off. All that was left of Don-Troop stood lined up in the twilight with their kit-bags beside them, awaiting the last order.

" Mount ! . . ." shouted the sergeant-major.

The men clambered up. The three lorries passed slowly out of the courtyard, down the road over the causeway, and so to the outer gate of the Fort.

A little figure in black was standing by the roadside outside the gate. It was Carmela. She had walked all the way from Valetta to give Doughy a pleasant surprise when he left the Fort on commencing his leave. Ignorant of what had happened she had patiently waited on, expecting to see him emerge at any moment.

The sudden exit of the vehicles packed with troops puzzled her. She scanned them closely for a sign of Doughy as they crawled slowly out of the gate.

One . . . Two . . .

The third and last was approaching. As it turned into the main road she ran by the side of it, anxiously examining the faces of the men.

Smiler sat in the rear of the last lorry. He saw Carmela and tried to shield himself from her glance. But she recognised him.

" Smee-ler," she cried. " Erry . . . Where is ? "

He opened his mouth to say something but was more dumb than Doughy had ever been. Carmela was still trotting behind the lorry, looking up at him appealingly.

Suddenly, without a word, he leaned over and thrust something into her hand. The lorry gathered pace.

The last he saw of her was a forlorn little figure dressed in black, standing in the twilight in the middle of the deserted road, untying a pocket-handkerchief.

## XIII—Epilogue

So ends the story of Fort Pedro as it concerns Don-Troop, Doughy, Smiler, the Colonel, the Gun Position Officer and the rest of them. But for Fort Pedro itself, it was far from being the end of the story. It was merely the end of a chapter. For Fort Pedro's story was but a part of Malta's story. And Malta's story was destined to have a victorious ending.

Fort Pedro, rising phœnix-like from its dust and ruins, once more took its place in the battle-line. Within a fortnight infantry parties had filled in the worst of the bomb-craters and created some sort of order out of chaos. New gun-pits were constructed. New guns took the place of those beyond the skill of Ordnance shops to repair. New gun-crews manned them. But it was the same old defiance they thundered against the onslaughts of the Luftwaffe.

Moreover, Fort Pedro had weathered the worst. Better days were in store for all. The month ended with the A.A. gunners' bag numbering 256 planes for the year. More and more Spitfires arrived to relieve the gun-sites of some of the burden of defence. A big convoy fought its way through bringing much needed supplies of munitions to the hard-pressed garrison. And the admiration with which the whole Empire watched Malta's dauntless resistance was fitly symbolised in the award of the George Cross.

October brought the utter rout of Rommel, hundreds of miles away at El Alamein—a victory for Malta as much as for the Eighth Army itself. The long pursuit followed, across Libya, Tripoli and on into Tunisia. A new day dawned for Malta and her garrison. From being a lonely outpost of defence she became a spearhead of attack. Day and night her planes went forth to bomb the Luftwaffe in its own lairs. And in the gardens of the Palace of Sant' Antonio the nurse-maids once more sat with their perambulators gossiping under the orange trees.

From the scarred and long suffering island a British army embarked to invade Sicily—a reversal of fortunes such as could never have been contemplated by Don-Troop on that black Sunday afternoon, barely twelve months before, when at Fort Pedro their corner of the world seemed to be tumbling about their ears.

The enemy was driven out of Sicily.    Italy itself was invaded. . . .

And so on, till Malta's crowning day of all.    That triumphant day when the bastions and *barraccas* of Valetta were once more thick with crowds, the same crowds that in the dark days had gathered there watching in anxious silence the bomb-riddled *Illustrious* seek sanctuary in Grand Harbour.

Now they were cheering.    Cheers like the echoes of Grand Harbour Barrage itself.    And while they cheered the surrendered Italian Fleet cast anchor on the deep blue waters of the Harbour.

THE END

GUN BUSTER is the literary discovery of the war. His first book *RETURN VIA DUNKIRK* "is deeply moving in its stark realism. The spirit is there ; the book is full of spirit—the spirit of the B.E.F.—with its good humour, its bravery, its amazing power of endurance and recovery."—*The Sunday Times.*
" The most vivid, moving, yet glorious book I have so far read of the fighting in France which led eventually to the epic of Dunkirk."—*The Tatler.*

His second book *BATTLE DRESS* is " a gallant book. The stories are exciting. Their themes range from the humdrum to the heroic, their characters from Brass Hats to the rank and file, their scenes from beleaguered shell-holes to the inferno of Dunkirk. This excellent book will confirm the reputation won by the writer with *RETURN VIA DUNKIRK* its vivid predecessor." — HORACE HORSNELL, *The Observer.*

His third book *ZERO HOURS* " gives us an exciting picturesque series of desert war incidents full of terror, of humour and character . . . admirable first hand accounts."—*The Daily Sketch.*